Maths

Age 7-8

Contents

Activities

2   Number sequences
3   Place value
4   Addition and subtraction
5   Subtraction
6   2-D shapes
7   Ordering numbers
8   Calendars
9   Fractions
10 Measuring length
11 Multiplication facts
12 Addition
13 Sorting diagrams
14 Measuring mass
15 Money
16 Measuring perimeter

17 Addition and subtraction problems
18 Symmetry
19 Measuring capacity
20 Division
21 3-D shapes
22 Mental addition
23 Equivalent fractions
24 Adding and subtracting fractions
25 Mental subtraction
26 Money problems
27 Right angles
28 Time
29 Handling data
30 Odd and even numbers
31 Numbers to 1000

Quick Tests

32 Test 1 Place value
33 Test 2 Addition and subtraction
34 Test 3 Word problems:
    addition and subtraction
35 Test 4 2-D shapes
36 Test 5 Numbers: counting
    and properties
37 Test 6 Multiplication tables
38 Test 7 Money (1)
39 Test 8 Fractions (1)
40 Test 9 Time (1)
41 Test 10 Data handling
42 Test 11 Finding 10 or 100
    more or less
43 Test 12 Addition
44 Test 13 Word problems:
    multiplication and division
45 Test 14 3-D shapes

46 Test 15 Measures and time
47 Test 16 Number patterns
48 Test 17 Multiplication and division
49 Test 18 Money (2)
50 Test 19 Fractions (2)
51 Test 20 Data (1)
52 Test 21 Telling the time with 12-
    and 24-hour clocks
53 Test 22 Subtraction
54 Test 23 Money problems
55 Test 24 Shapes: right angles
56 Test 25 Tenths
57 Test 26 Division
58 Test 27 Problems
59 Test 28 Multiplication
60 Test 29 Time (2)
61 Test 30 Data (2)

62 Answers

Paul Broadbent and Peter Patilla

Number sequences

Look at the difference between numbers in a **sequence**.

This will help you to spot any **patterns**.

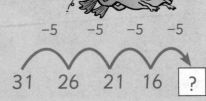

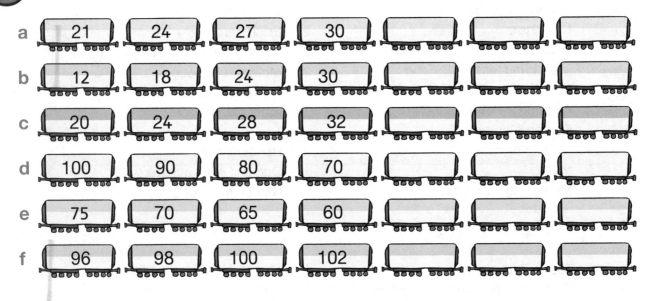

The next number is 23.

The next number is 11.

1 Write the next three numbers in each sequence.

a 21 24 27 30

b 12 18 24 30

c 20 24 28 32

d 100 90 80 70

e 75 70 65 60

f 96 98 100 102

2 Continue the jumps. Write the next four new numbers in the sequence.

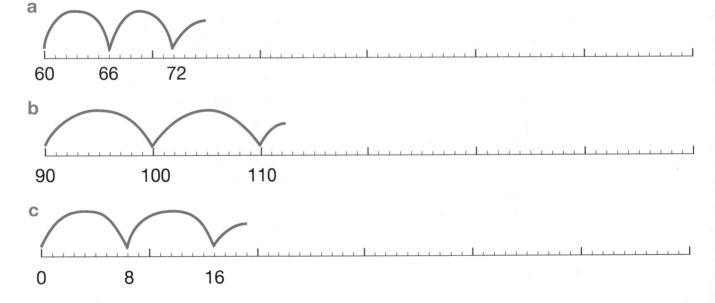

a
60 66 72

b
90 100 110

c
0 8 16

Place value

3-digit numbers are made from **hundreds**, **tens** and **ones**.

hundreds   tens   ones

436 = 400 + 30 + 6

The position of the digits 0 to 9 gives the value of the number.

1 Write the missing numbers.

a 482 = 400 + ☐ + 2

b 745 = 700 + 40 + ☐

c 193 = ☐ + 90 + ☐

d 216 = 200 + ☐ + ☐

e 552 = ☐ + ☐ + 2

f 324 = ☐ + 20 + ☐

g 627 = ☐ + ☐ + ☐

h 813 = ☐ + ☐ + ☐

i 945 = ☐ + ☐ + ☐

j 799 = ☐ + ☐ + ☐

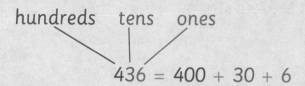

2 Read the number on the abacus. Add the number below and write the new number.

a
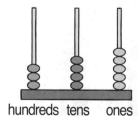
hundreds tens ones

Add 5 ☐

b
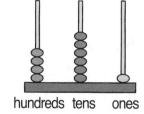
hundreds tens ones

Add 9 ☐

c
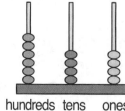
hundreds tens ones

Add 60 ☐

Addition and subtraction

If you learn the addition and subtraction facts to 20, they can help you to learn other facts. Look at these patterns.

$4 + 9 = 13$

$40 + 90 = 130$

$400 + 900 = 1300$

$15 - 8 = 7$

$150 - 80 = 70$

$1500 - 800 = 700$

5 + 7 = 12

1 Write the answers to these questions.

a $7 + 5$ =

$70 + 50$ =

$700 + 500$ =

b $9 + 6$ =

$90 + 60$ =

$900 + 600$ =

c $4 + 11$ =

$40 + 110$ =

$400 + 1100$ =

d $13 - 6$ =

$130 - 60$ =

$1300 - 600$ =

e $15 - 7$ =

$150 - 70$ =

$1500 - 700$ =

f $18 - 9$ =

$180 - 90$ =

$1800 - 900$ =

g $180 - 60$ =

h $800 + 500$ =

i $1700 - 400$ =

j $1200 + 600$ =

k $150 + 90$ =

l $130 - 90$ =

m $800 + 800$ =

2 Circle touching pairs of numbers that total 100. The pairs can be vertical or horizontal. You should find ten pairs.

34	51	59	41	76	82	38	62
66	75	25	65	24	47	53	77
91	19	72	83	17	45	96	13
24	81	74	56	35	55	48	52

Subtraction

When you subtract numbers, decide whether to use a **mental method**, or whether you need to use the **written method**.

Mental method 92 − 57 = 35

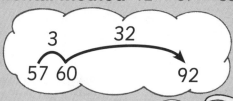

57 on to 60 is 3

60 on to 92 is 32

32 add 3 is 35

Written method 143 − 86 = 57

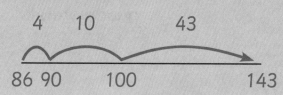

Count on from 86 in steps
4 + 10 + 43 = 57

These both use a number line to work out the answers.

1 Use the number line method for these.

a 74 − 38 = ☐

38 ————————————— 74

c 93 − 57 = ☐

57 ————————————— 93

e 152 − 76 = ☐

76 ————————————— 152

b 81 − 46 = ☐

46 ————————————— 81

d 125 − 87 = ☐

87 ————————————— 125

f 164 − 95 = ☐

95 ————————————— 164

2 Choose a method to work out the differences between these pairs of weights.

a

Difference: ☐ kg

c

Difference: ☐ kg

e
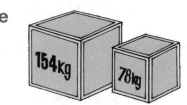

Difference: ☐ kg

b

Difference: ☐ kg

d
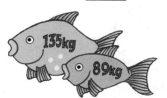

Difference: ☐ kg

f

Difference: ☐ kg

2-D shapes

3-sided shapes are **triangles**.

4-sided shapes are **quadrilaterals**.

5-sided shapes are **pentagons**.

6-sided shapes are **hexagons**.

circle   semi-circle   oval

1 Cross the odd one out in each set. Name each set of shapes.

a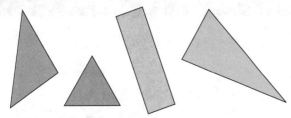

_____

c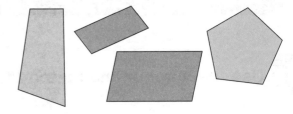

_____

b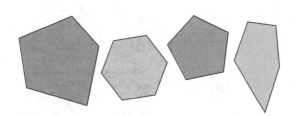

_____

d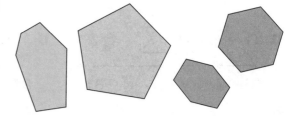

_____

2 There are two shapes in this box that are not in the red box. Colour the two shapes.

There are two shapes in this box that are not in the blue box. Colour the two shapes.

Ordering numbers

When you put 3-digit numbers in **order**, look at the **hundreds** first, then the **tens** and then the **ones** digit.

785 grams is heavier than 758 grams.

7**8**5 g
7**5**8 g   8 tens is more than 5 tens.

---

1 Write these in order, smallest first.

a
207 cm   87 cm
137 cm
170 cm
107 cm

b
225 ml 308 ml
340 ml
275 ml 272 ml

c
£1 and 70p
£1 and 95p
£1 and 38p
£2 and 5p
£1 and 9p

d
802 m   635 m
525 m
610 m   608 m

---

2 These number cards were in order. Colour the two cards that have been changed over.

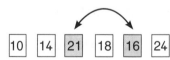

10 14 21 18 16 24

a 7   11   15   19   17   16   21

b 23   28   34   39   48   42   56

c 63   52   57   36   71   74   82

d 108   114   123   184   215   212   206

Calendars

A calendar shows **dates**.

It usually shows:

- the day
- the date
- the month
- the year.

There are 12 months in a year.

JANUARY	FEBRUARY	MARCH	APRIL
MAY	JUNE	JULY	AUGUST
SEPTEMBER	OCTOBER	NOVEMBER	DECEMBER

1 Use this calendar to help answer these questions.

a What is the month? _____

b On which day is the 22nd? _____

c What date is the
second Friday? _____

d What date is one week after
the 19th? _____

e On which day is the
30th April? _____

f On which day is the
2nd June? _____

May 2004

S	M	T	W	T	F	S
						1
2	3	4	5	6	7	8
9	10	11	12	13	14	15
16	17	18	19	20	21	22
23	24	25	26	27	28	29
30	31					

2 Learn this method for remembering the number of days in each month.

a Hold your hands in front of you,
so you can see your knuckles.

b Start with January from the left
knuckle of your little finger.

c Move to the right, with February in
the gap, March the next knuckle
and so on.

d All the knuckle months have
31 days.

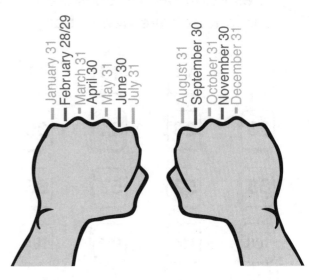

January 31
February 28/29
March 31
April 30
May 31
June 30
July 31
August 31
September 30
October 31
November 30
December 31

Fractions

Fractions show the number of **equal parts** of a whole.

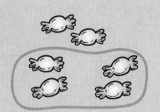

This shows three-tenths or $\frac{3}{10}$. It is one whole divided into ten equal parts. Three parts are shaded.

$\frac{2}{3}$ of 6 = 4

1 Colour the shapes to show each fraction.

a $\frac{3}{4}$

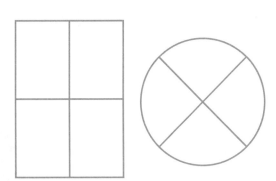

c $\frac{3}{5}$

b $\frac{2}{3}$

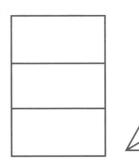

d $\frac{7}{10}$

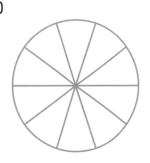

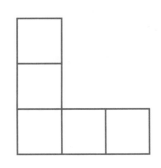

2 Write the answers to these.

a $\frac{3}{4}$ of 12 = ☐

b $\frac{1}{8}$ of 16 = ☐

c $\frac{3}{10}$ of 40 = ☐

d $\frac{2}{3}$ of 15 = ☐

e $\frac{4}{5}$ of 30 = ☐

f $\frac{1}{12}$ of 24 = ☐

g $\frac{3}{4}$ of 20 = ☐

h $\frac{2}{3}$ of 21 = ☐

Measuring length

Practise measuring things to the nearest $\frac{1}{2}$ centimetre.

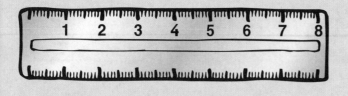

An **estimate** is a rough answer without measuring.

If you estimated this line to be about 5 or 6 cm, that is a very good estimate.

This line is about $5\frac{1}{2}$ cm long.

1 Use a ruler to measure each length to the nearest half centimetre.

a ▬▬▬▬▬▬▬ ☐ cm

b ▬▬▬▬▬▬▬▬▬▬▬ ☐ cm

c ▬▬▬▬▬▬▬ ☐ cm

d ▬▬▬▬▬▬▬▬▬ ☐ cm

e ▬▬▬▬▬ ☐ cm

f ▬▬▬▬▬▬▬▬▬▬▬ ☐ cm

2 Use a ruler to draw a line for each measurement.

a 5 cm ➜

b 8 cm ➜

c 10 cm ➜

Multiplication facts

Try to learn these **multiplication** tables.

×	0	1	2	3	4	5	6	7	8	9	10	11	12
2	0	2	4	6	8	10	12	14	16	18	20	22	24
3	0	3	6	9	12	15	18	21	24	27	30	33	36
4	0	4	8	12	16	20	24	28	32	36	40	44	48
5	0	5	10	15	20	25	30	35	40	45	50	55	60
8	0	8	16	24	32	40	48	56	64	72	80	88	96
10	0	10	20	30	40	50	60	70	80	90	100	110	120
11	0	11	22	33	44	55	66	77	88	99	110	121	132
12	0	12	24	36	48	60	72	84	96	108	120	132	144

$4 \times 5 = 20$

$5 \times 4 = 20$

The order does not matter.

1 **Answer these as quickly as you can.**

a 10×2 = ☐

10×7 = ☐

10×8 = ☐

10×10 = ☐

3×10 = ☐

9×10 = ☐

b 5×2 = ☐

5×7 = ☐

5×8 = ☐

6×5 = ☐

3×5 = ☐

9×5 = ☐

c 2×2 = ☐

2×7 = ☐

2×8 = ☐

6×2 = ☐

3×2 = ☐

9×2 = ☐

d 6×8 = ☐

4×7 = ☐

4×8 = ☐

11×4 = ☐

3×12 = ☐

8×8 = ☐

e 4×12 = ☐

7×8 = ☐

11×5 = ☐

3×4 = ☐

3×8 = ☐

12×8 = ☐

2 **Answer these. Use the code to find the name of two cities in Scotland.**

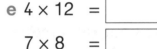

a 4×5 5×5 7×3 10×2 6×4 8×3

☐ ☐ ☐ ☐ ☐ ☐

b 4×6 2×10 4×4 3×7 5×7 5×5 3×10 8×5 6×3

☐ ☐ ☐ ☐ ☐ ☐ ☐ ☐ ☐

Addition

When you add numbers, decide whether to use a **mental method**, or whether you need to use the **written method**.

Mental method 53 + 48

Example

> 53 add 50 is 103
> Take away 2 is 101

> 53 add 40 is 93
> 93 add 8 is 101

Written method 156 + 75

Example

```
  1 5 6
+   7 5
-------
  2 3 1
  1   1
```

Add the ones (6 + 5)

Then the tens
(50 + 70 + 10)

Then the hundreds
(100 + 100)

1 Use your own methods to add these. Colour the star if you used a mental method.

a 51 + 43 = ☆

b 38 + 63 = ☆

c 29 + 35 = ☆

d 86 + 62 = ☆

e 91 + 74 = ☆

f 57 + 69 = ☆

g 37 + 94 = ☆

h 75 + 66 = ☆

i 88 + 83 = ☆

j 124 + 132 = ☆

k 146 + 105 = ☆

l 135 + 166 = ☆

2 Answer these.

a
```
  3 8 6
+   5 8
-------
```

b
```
  2 7 4
+   8 1
-------
```

c
```
  5 4 6
+   7 4
-------
```

d
```
  9 1 4
+   8 7
-------
```

e
```
  6 7 6
+   7 8
-------
```

f
```
  7 2 7
+   8 3
-------
```

386
+58

Sorting diagrams

Compare these **sorting diagrams** for numbers to 10.

Venn diagram	**Carroll diagram**	**Tree diagram**
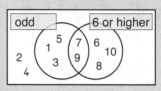		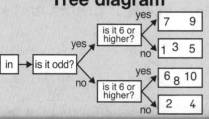

1 Draw these shapes in the correct parts of each diagram.

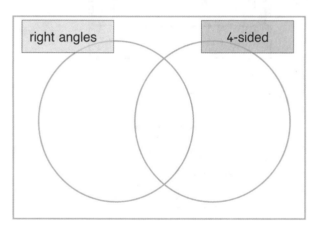

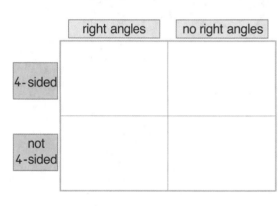

a

right angles   4-sided

b

	right angles	no right angles
4-sided		
not 4-sided		

2 This diagram sorts numbers.

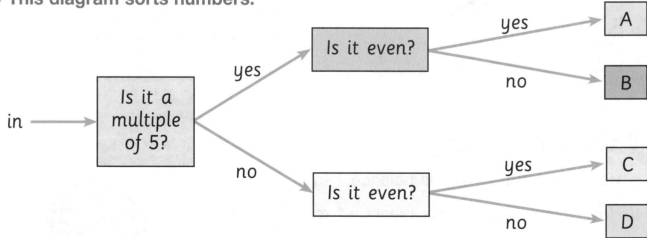

Into which boxes will these numbers be sorted?

a 27 → ☐   b 18 → ☐   c 40 → ☐   d 25 → ☐   e 30 → ☐

Measuring mass

We find the **mass** or **weight** of an object using scales.

We weigh in **grams** and **kilograms**.

1000 grams = 1 kilogram

1000 g = 1 kg

---

1 Write the mass shown on each of these.

a
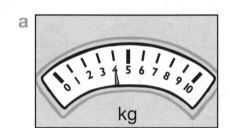
kg [ ] kg

d
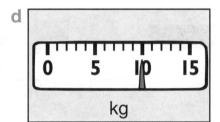
kg [ ] kg

b
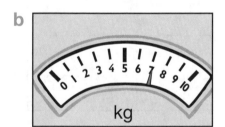
kg [ ] kg

e
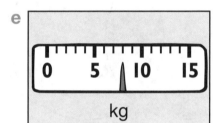
kg [ ] kg

c
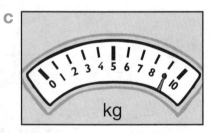
kg [ ] kg

f
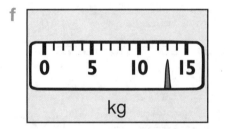
kg [ ] kg

---

2 Answer these questions.

a How many 100 g weights balance 1 kg? [ ]

b How many 500 g weights balance 1 kg? [ ]

c How many 200 g weights balance 1 kg? [ ]

d How many 250 g weights balance 1 kg? [ ]

e How many 50 g weights balance 500 g? [ ]

Money

There are **100 pence in £1**.

£1	=	100p
£2 and 60p	=	260p
£1 and 35p	=	135p
£3 and 9p	=	309p

1 Write the coin values in the circles to show the fewest number of coins you would give for items at these prices.

a **80p** ◯ ◯ ◯   e **£1 and 45p** ◯ ◯ ◯ ◯

b **£1 and 15p** ◯ ◯ ◯   f **£1 and 80p** ◯ ◯ ◯ ◯

c **£2 and 55p** ◯ ◯ ◯   g **£2 and 35p** ◯ ◯ ◯ ◯

d **£3 and 10p** ◯ ◯ ◯   h **£4 and 55p** ◯ ◯ ◯ ◯

2 Draw coins in the empty purse. It should contain half the number of coins as the other purse but the same total amount of money.

a

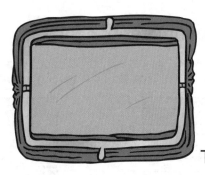

Total: 70p

Total: 70p

b

Total: £ [ ]

and [ ] p

Total: £ [ ]

and [ ] p

15

Measuring perimeter

The perimeter of a shape is the **distance all around the edge**.

The perimeter of this triangle is
3 cm + 4 cm + 5 cm = 12 cm

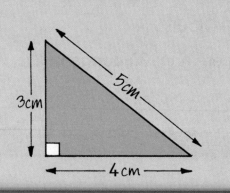

1 Use a ruler to measure the perimeter of each shape.

a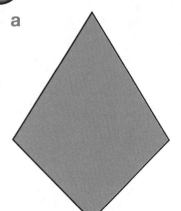

b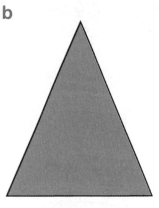

c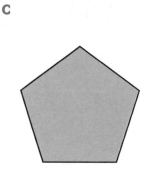

d

Perimeter = _____

Perimeter = _____

Perimeter = _____

Perimeter = _____

2 Write the perimeter of each rectangle.

a Perimeter: [ ] cm

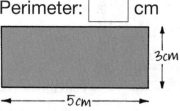
5cm 3cm

b Perimeter: [ ] cm

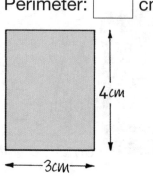
4cm 3cm

c Perimeter: [ ] cm

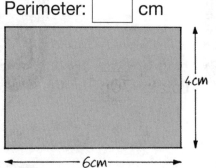
4cm 6cm

d Perimeter: [ ] cm

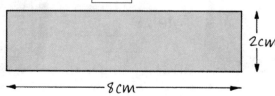
2cm 8cm

e Perimeter: [ ] cm

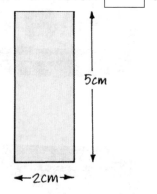
5cm 2cm

Addition and subtraction problems

Here are some **addition** words:

altogether   more   add
total   plus   sum

Here are some **subtraction** words:

subtract   leaves   minus
take away   difference   less

1 Answer these questions.

a What is the sum of
30 and 50?

b What is the total of the
first four odd numbers?

c What is the difference
between 70 and 110?

d What is 16 more than 25?

e Which number is 9
less than 22?

f What is 45 take away 20?

g What is the total of
80, 90, 100?

h What is 500 minus 150?

2 Try these money problems.

a Circle the **three** presents that can
be bought for exactly £1.

b Join the **four** presents that can be
bought for exactly £1 and 50p.

Symmetry

A **line of symmetry** shows where a **mirror line** could be drawn.

One half of the shape is a **reflection** of the other half.

These have 1 line of symmetry.   These have 2 lines of symmetry.

1 Draw the line or lines of symmetry on each shape.

a

c

e

g

b

d

f

h

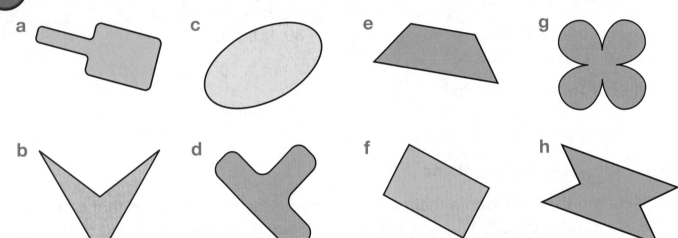

2 Draw and colour the reflection of each shape.

a   b

Measuring capacity

We measure the capacity of containers in **millilitres** and **litres**.

1000 millilitres = 1 litre

1000 ml = 1 l

You can read the scale on the side of a jug carefully to work out the capacity.

1 Write how much liquid is in each container.

a

☐ ml

c

☐ ml

e

☐ ml

b

☐ ml

d

☐ ml

f

☐ ml

2 Answer these.

a 1 litre = ☐ ml

b $\frac{1}{2}$ litre = ☐ ml

c $\frac{1}{4}$ litre = ☐ ml

d $\frac{1}{10}$ litre = ☐ ml

e How many 200 ml bottles will fill a 1 litre jug? ☐

f How many 50 ml bottles will fill a 500 ml jug? ☐

Division

Sometimes when you **divide** there is an amount **left over**.

This is called a **remainder**.

If you wanted to share 7 sweets between 3 people, they would each have 2 sweets with 1 left over.

$$7 \div 3 = 2 \text{ remainder } 1$$

1 Group these and write the answers.

a  $13 \div 2 = \boxed{}$ remainder $\boxed{}$

b  $22 \div 5 = \boxed{}$ remainder $\boxed{}$

c  $17 \div 3 = \boxed{}$ remainder $\boxed{}$

d  $15 \div 4 = \boxed{}$ remainder $\boxed{}$

e $16 \div 5 = \boxed{}$ remainder $\boxed{}$

f $20 \div 3 = \boxed{}$ remainder $\boxed{}$

2 Draw lines to join these to the correct remainder.

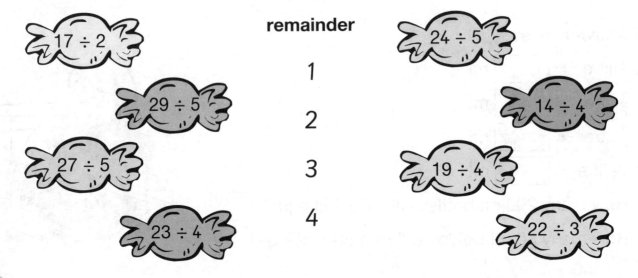

remainder

17 ÷ 2   24 ÷ 5

1

29 ÷ 5   14 ÷ 4

2

27 ÷ 5   19 ÷ 4

3

23 ÷ 4   22 ÷ 3

4

3-D shapes

Learn the names of these shapes.

cube   cone   pyramid   sphere

cuboid   cylinder   prism

Prisms have:
* two end faces that are the same
* rectangular sides.

If you slice a prism into equal lengths, all the slices will be the same shape and size.

1 Write how many faces these shapes have. Name each shape.

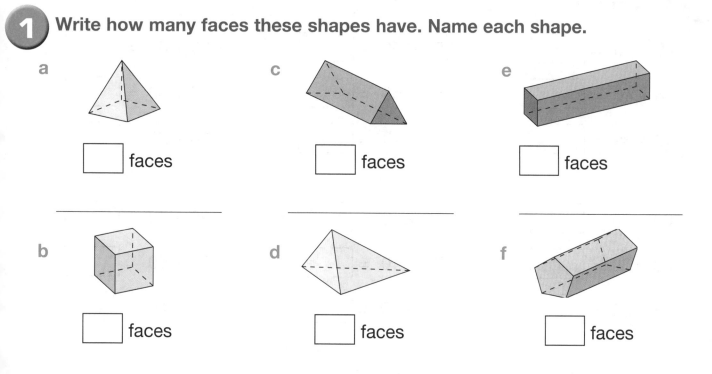

a [ ] faces

_____

c [ ] faces

_____

e [ ] faces

_____

b [ ] faces

_____

d [ ] faces

_____

f [ ] faces

_____

2 Write the letter for each shape in the correct part of the Carroll diagram.

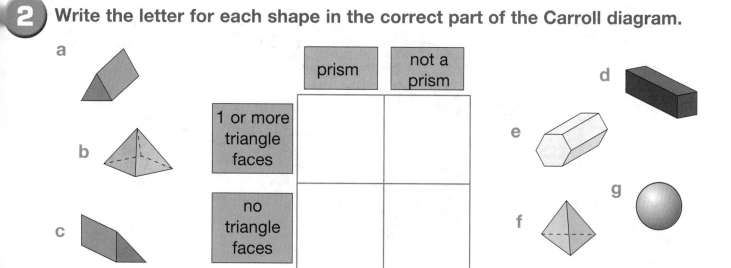

	prism	not a prism
1 or more triangle faces		
no triangle faces		

21

Mental addition

Adding **larger numbers** can be easy if you are quick at adding **small numbers**.

$$4 + 3 = 7$$
$$40 + 30 = 70$$
$$45 + 30 = 75$$

Adding numbers such as 19, 29, 39 ... can be worked out like this.

$$45 + 29$$
$$\downarrow$$
$$45 + 30 - 1 = 75 - 1 = 74$$

1 Answer these.

a 40 + 40 =

46 + 40 =

46 + 39 =

c 50 + 50 =

54 + 50 =

54 + 49 =

e 80 + 30 =

86 + 30 =

86 + 29 =

b 60 + 30 =

63 + 30 =

63 + 29 =

d 70 + 40 =

75 + 40 =

75 + 39 =

f 90 + 50 =

94 + 50 =

94 + 49 =

2 Draw lines to join pairs that total 100.

22

Equivalent fractions

Some fractions are **equivalent**.

This means they look different, but are worth the same value.

These are all equivalent to $\frac{1}{2}$.

$\frac{2}{4}$ $\frac{3}{6}$ $\frac{4}{8}$ $\frac{5}{10}$

1 Put a cross through the odd one out.

a

b

c

2 Write each fraction in two ways. The first one has been done for you.

a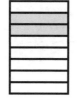

$\frac{2}{6}$ and $\frac{1}{3}$

c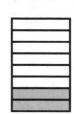

$\frac{}{}$ and $\frac{}{}$

e

$\frac{}{}$ and $\frac{}{}$

b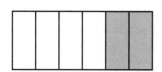

$\frac{}{}$ and $\frac{}{}$

d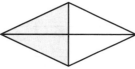

$\frac{}{}$ and $\frac{}{}$

f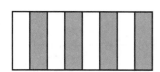

$\frac{}{}$ and $\frac{}{}$

Adding and subtracting fractions

Like fractions are fractions with the same **denominator** (bottom number). You can add and subtract like fractions easily. Simply add or subtract the **numerators** (top numbers) and then write answer over the **common denominator**.

Find $\frac{1}{5} + \frac{2}{5}$

$\frac{1}{5} + \frac{2}{5} = \frac{3}{5}$

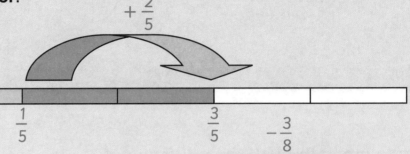

Find $\frac{7}{8} - \frac{3}{8}$

$\frac{7}{8} - \frac{3}{8} = \frac{4}{8} = \frac{1}{2}$

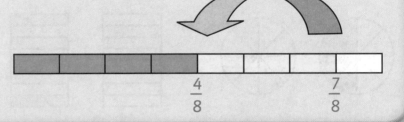

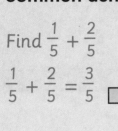 **1** Answer these fraction calculations giving the answer in the simplest form. Use the bars to help you.

a $\frac{5}{7} + \frac{2}{7}$ =

b $\frac{2}{6} + \frac{1}{6}$ =

c $\frac{1}{4} + \frac{2}{4}$ =

d $\frac{4}{15} + \frac{6}{15}$ =

e $\frac{1}{9} + \frac{4}{9}$ =

f $\frac{13}{14} - \frac{1}{14}$ =

g $\frac{5}{8} - \frac{2}{8}$ =

h $\frac{3}{7} - \frac{2}{7}$ =

i $\frac{9}{18} - \frac{3}{18}$ =

j $\frac{9}{12} - \frac{3}{12}$ =

Mental subtraction

What is 54 − 28?

A good way of working this out in your head is to **count on**.

28 on to 30 is 2
30 on to 54 is 24
24 add 2 is 26
so 54 − 28 = 26

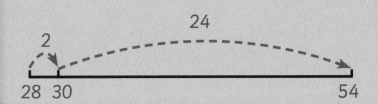

24

2

28 30   54

1 Answer these questions.

a 40 − 28 =   e 46 − 28 =   i 55 − 29 =

b 70 − 39 =   f 44 − 19 =   j 64 − 39 =

c 90 − 47 =   g 53 − 27 =   k 56 − 37 =

d 38 − 29 =   h 61 − 38 =   l 62 − 47 =

2 The difference between two numbers that are next to each other is written in the box above them. Write the missing numbers.

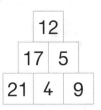

| 12 |
| 17 | 5 |
| 21 | 4 | 9 |

a

| | | |
| 26 | 12 | 18 |

b

| 3 |
| 14 | |
| | 7 | 18 |

c

21	13
	6	

d

| 9 |
| | 6 |
| | 3 |

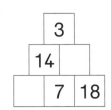
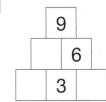
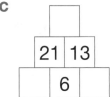

Money problems

You often need to work out how much **change** is needed.

To calculate change, count on from the price of the item to the amount of money given.

£1 and 40p → 10p → £1 and 50p → 50p → £2

The change from £2 is 60p.

1 Write the answers to these money problems.

a Work out the change from £1.

b Work out the change from £2.

c Work out the change from £5.

 75p change: ☐ p

 £1 and 60p change: ☐ p

 £3 and 50p change: £ ☐

 68p change: ☐ p

 £1 and 25p change: ☐ p

 £2 and 80p change: £ ☐

89p change: ☐ p

 £1 and 85p change: ☐ p

 £1 and 90p change: £ ☐

2 Answer the money problems.

£2 and 60p
£2 and 80p
£2 and 40p

a Leon buys 2 books. They cost £2 and £2 and 20p. How much change will he receive from £5?

☐

b Alexis bought a CD. She had 20p change from a £10 note. How much was her CD?

☐

c Which 2 items when bought together will cost £5?

_____

d What will be the total cost of all 3 items?

☐

Right angles

A right angle is a **quarter of a turn**.

A **complete turn** is the same as **four right angles**.

Here are four compass directions.

You can turn **clockwise**

or **anticlockwise**

---

1 Tick each right angle.

a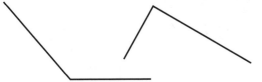

b

---

2 Write the direction you will face after turning.

a Start facing north. Turn 1 right angle anticlockwise.

_____

b Start facing east. Turn 1 right angle clockwise.

_____

c Start facing west. Turn 2 right angles clockwise.

_____

d Start facing south. Turn 3 right angles anticlockwise.

_____

Time

On a clock face, read the **minutes past the hour** to tell the time.

As the minute hand moves around the clock, the hour hand moves towards the next hour.

 5:42

42 minutes past 5
or 18 minutes to 6

 9:18

18 minutes past 9

1 Write the times shown on each clock.

a   b   c    d

_____   _____   _____   _____

Draw the hands on these clocks.

e    f    g    h

7.56   9.03   3.41   11.18

2 Write the number of minutes between each of these times.

a

[ ] minutes

c

[ ] minutes

b

[ ] minutes

d

[ ] minutes

Handling data

Some graphs use **bars** or **columns** to show information.

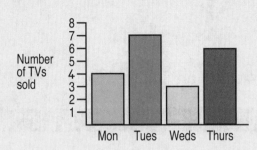

Number of TVs sold

Mon Tues Weds Thurs

Pictograms use pictures to show information.

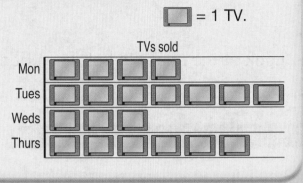

☐ = 1 TV.

TVs sold

Mon
Tues
Weds
Thurs

---

1 This graph shows the number of hours a group of children watch television in a week.

a Who watched television the most? _____

b How many hours did Gemma watch? _____

c How many more hours of television did Laura watch than Kate? _____

d How many fewer hours did Ali watch than Joe? _____

e Which two children watched the same amount of television?

_____ and _____

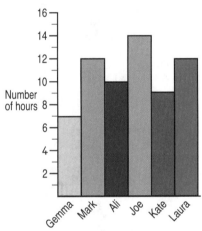

Number of hours

Gemma Mark Ali Joe Kate Laura

---

2 Carry out a TV watching survey.

- Ask family or friends to work out how many hours of TV they watch in a week.

- Record your results as a pictogram.

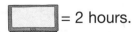 = 2 hours.

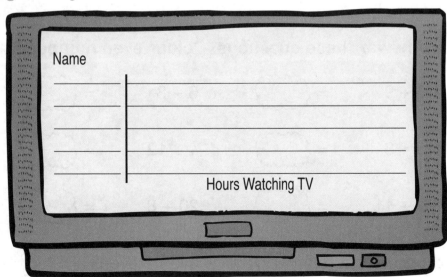

Name

Hours Watching TV

Odd and even numbers

Odd numbers always end in

1 3 5 7 9

Even numbers always end in

0 2 4 6 8

Look at the ones digit of a number:

14**5** is odd   15**4** is even

1 Colour all the odd numbers red.

74	46	108	94	114	136	28	150	96
102	85	77	109	192	59	261	395	128
314	61	100	205	116	299	94	105	306
108	93	209	183	318	417	89	101	200
52	74	82	211	260	300	192	245	412
112	196	418	309	234	108	386	193	350
376	190	210	106	92	34	76	84	272

What odd number do the red squares create?

2 Answer these questions. Colour even numbers blue and odd numbers red.

a 7 + 9 =

b 5 + 3 =

c 9 + 11 =

d odd + odd =

e 6 + 8 =

f 4 + 12 =

g 20 + 8 =

h even + even =

i 7 + 4 =

j 9 + 10 =

k 15 + 2 =

l odd + even =

Numbers to *1000*

3-digit numbers are made from **hundreds, tens** and **ones**.

hundreds   tens   ones

460 → 400 + 60

1 Complete this table. The first row has been done for you.

143	100 + 40 + 3	one hundred and forty-three	hundreds tens ones
251			hundreds tens ones
	700 + 30 + 6		hundreds tens ones
			hundreds tens ones
		nine hundred and seventy-six	hundreds tens ones

2 Use the digits 3 4 6.

a How many different 3-digit numbers can you make? _____

b Write them in order, starting with the smallest.

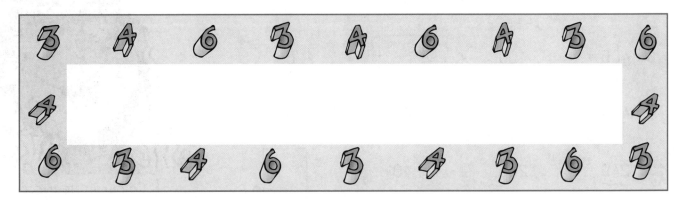

Test 1 Place value

There are **10 digits** which are **0, 1, 2, 3, 4, 5, 6, 7, 8** and **9**.
Digits are used to build up larger numbers.
The position of a digit in a number changes its value.

hundreds	tens	ones	
6	3	1	= 600 + 30 + 1
3	1	4	= 300 + 10 + 4

Write the numbers to match the words.

1. sixty ⟹ ☐

2. six hundred and sixty ⟹ ☐

3. six hundred and six ⟹ ☐

4. sixteen ⟹ ☐

5. six hundred and sixty-six ⟹ ☐

Write the missing numbers.

6. 633 = 600 + 30 + ☐

7. 910 = ☐ + 10 + 0

8. 405 = 400 + ☐ + 5

9. 468 = ☐ + 60 + 8

10. 249 = 200 + 40 + ☐

Colour in your score

Test 2 Addition and subtraction

Knowing **number facts** can help you
to work out other calculations.

7 + 6 = 13

70 + 60 = 130

700 + 600 = 1300

12 − 6 = 6

120 − 60 = 60

1200 − 600 = 600

Answer these.

1. 40 + 70 =

2. 90 − 30 =

3. 130 − 50 =

4. 600 + 800 =

5. 900 − 400 =

6. 1200 + 500 =

7. 900 + 700 =

8. 170 − 80 =

9. 190 − 120 =

10. 800 + 500 =

Colour in your score

Test 3 Word problems: addition and subtraction

Learn these **addition** words:

altogether · TOTAL · **sum** · add · more than · greater than · **plus**

Learn these **subtraction** words:

less than · take away · **minus** · subtract · LEAVES · fewer than · **difference**

Answer these questions.

1. Which number is 173 minus 5?

2. What is the sum of 234 and 40?

3. What is 572 take away 200?

4. What number is 30 less than 272?

5. What is 432 add 500?

6. Tom goes shopping with £2.
   He spends 80p. How much does
   he have left?

7. Nigel has 75 points and Alison
   has 35. How many more points
   has Nigel?

8. Peta has 16 sweets. She eats 4 and
   gives 8 to Jan. How many sweets
   does she have left?

9. Ellen and Joe spend 87p each. How
   much do they spend altogether?

10. Rebecca has £2 and 75p. Her friend
    gives her 15p. How much money
    does Rebecca have now?

Colour in your score

10 · 9 · 8 · 7 · 6 · 5 · 4 · 3 · 2 · 1

Test 4 **2-D shapes**

Name	Number of sides
triangle	3
quadrilateral	4
pentagon	5
hexagon	6
heptagon	7
octagon	8

Write the name of each shape.

Draw one line of symmetry on each shape.

1. _____

2. _____

3. _____

4. _____

5. _____

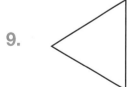

6.

7.

8.

9.

10.

10
9
8
7
6
5
4
3
2
1

Colour in your score

Test 5 Numbers: counting and properties

When you add a small number to a larger number, you can **count on**.
It is easier to count on from the larger number.

134 + 3 is easier to count than 3 + 134.

Add 4 to each number.

1. 89

2.  148

3. 707

4. 666

5.  415

Write the answers.

6.   40   +   912   =

7. 396   +   5   =

8. 700   +   108   =

9. 909   +   100   =

10.   70   +   644   =

10
9
8
7
6
5
4
3
2
1

Colour in your score

36

Test 6 Multiplication tables

When you **multiply numbers** the order does not matter.
Look at both numbers and choose which way you prefer.

5 × 7 has the **same answer** as 7 × 5.

2 × 8 has the **same answer** as 8 × 2.

Answer these.

1. 8 × 5 ⟹ ☐

2. 9 × 2 ⟹ ☐

3. 6 × 10 ⟹ ☐

4. 7 × 5 ⟹ ☐

5. 4 × 2 ⟹ ☐

6. 11 × 3 ⟹ ☐

7. 5 × 8 ⟹ ☐

8. 2 × 7 ⟹ ☐

9. 5 × 9 ⟹ ☐

10. 12 × 4 ⟹ ☐

Colour in your score

Test 7 Money (1)

Working out **change** need not be too difficult.
You must be able to make amounts up to **£1**.

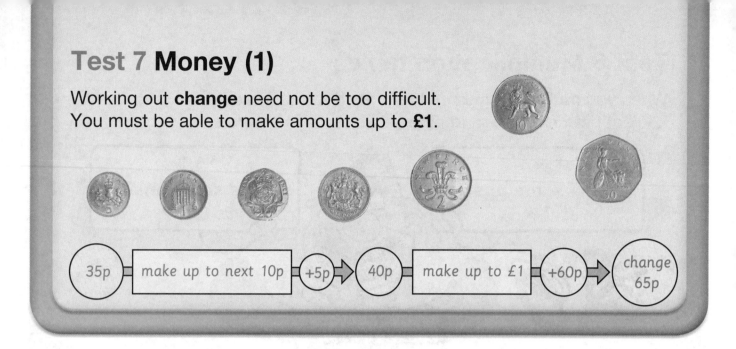

35p → make up to next 10p → +5p → 40p → make up to £1 → +60p → change 65p

Write the total amount of money in each piggybank.

The money in each purse is given to pay the price shown on each label. Write the change.

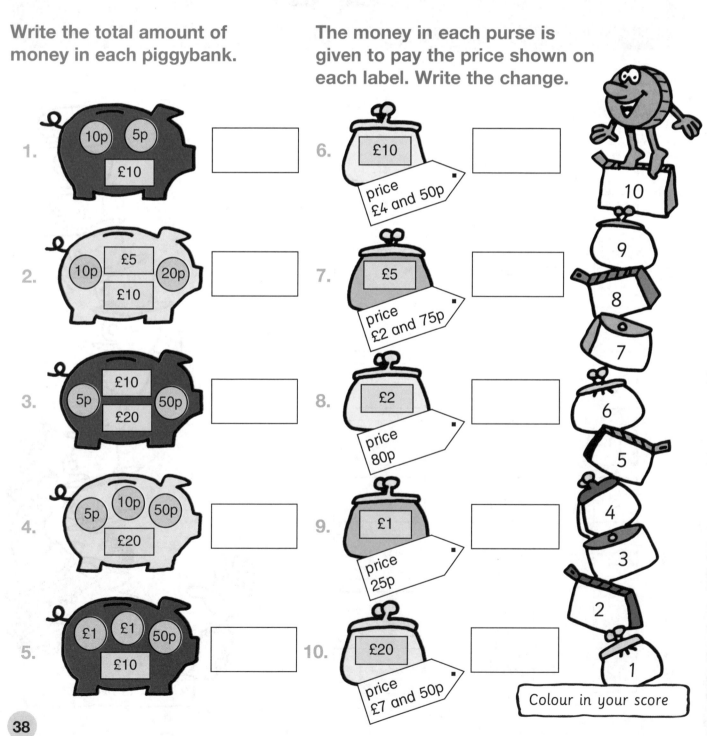

1. 10p 5p £10

2. £5 10p 20p £10

3. £10 5p 50p £20

4. 5p 10p 50p £20

5. £1 £1 50p £10

6. £10 — price £4 and 50p

7. £5 — price £2 and 75p

8. £2 — price 80p

9. £1 — price 25p

10. £20 — price £7 and 50p

10
9
8
7
6
5
4
3
2
1

Colour in your score

38

Test 8 Fractions (1)

Some **fractions** are **equivalent**. This means they are worth the same.

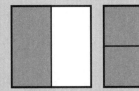 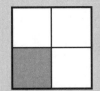 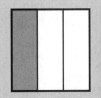

$$\frac{1}{2} = \frac{2}{4}$$ $$\frac{1}{4} = \frac{2}{8}$$ $$\frac{1}{3} = \frac{2}{6}$$

Write each fraction in two ways.

1. _____ and _____

2. _____ and _____

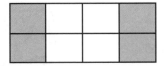

3. _____ and _____

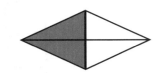

4. _____ and _____

5. _____ and _____

Colour these fractions.

6. $\frac{2}{3}$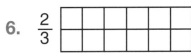

7. $\frac{1}{5}$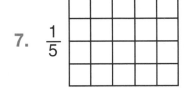

8. $\frac{7}{10}$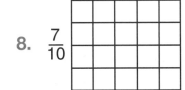

9. $\frac{3}{4}$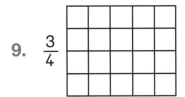

10. $\frac{1}{6}$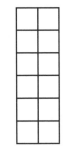

Colour in your score

39

Test 9 Time (1)

It is sometimes important to work out **the difference between two times**. Time is a way of measuring how long something lasts, or how long before things start or come to an end.

To find the difference between two times use a number line.

The first lesson began at 8:10 and ended at 9:20. How long was the lesson?

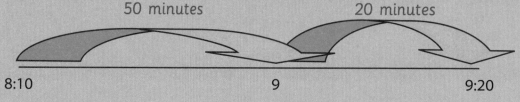

50 minutes   20 minutes

8:10   9   9:20

50 minutes + 20 minutes = 70 minutes = 1 hour 10 minutes

Read this information and then answer the questions below.

Baker Pat arrived at the bakery at 6.50.
He started to bake some cookies at 7.05.
The cookies were put in the oven at 7.35.
The cookies were ready at 8.05 and then left to cool for 15 minutes.
Icing the cookies finished at 8:40.
Baker Pat immediately started putting the cookies on a tray and had them all on at 8.55, and tidied up!
The bakery opened at 9:00 and closed at midday.

1. How long did the cookies take to bake in the oven? _____

2. How long did it take the baker to ice the cookies? _____

3. How long did it take the baker to place the cookies on the tray?

   _____

4. How many minutes did the baker have to tidy up before the bakery opened? _____

5. How long was the bakery open for? _____

Draw the hands on each clock to show the time.

6. | 8.55 | 7. | 3.45 | 8. | 10.35 | 9. | 12.40 | 10. | 1.05 |

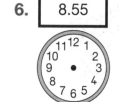

Colour in your score

Test 10 Data handling

In a Venn diagram the area **outside** the circles is also important.

Things which are coloured **and** triangles go in the overlap.

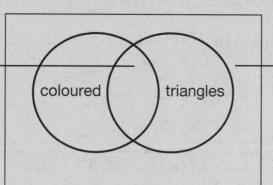

coloured   triangles

Things which are not coloured **and** not triangles go outside the circles.

Draw each shape on this diagram.

1.

2.

3.

4.

5.

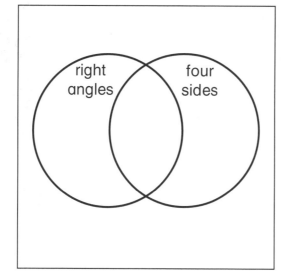

right angles   four sides

Draw each shape on this diagram.

6.

7.

8.

9.

10.

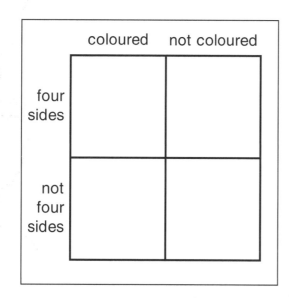

	coloured	not coloured
four sides		
not four sides		

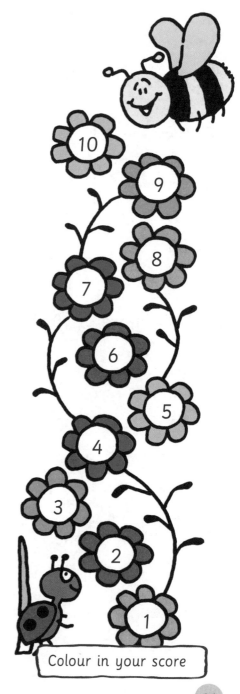

Colour in your score

Test 11 Finding 10 or 100 more or less

When we find **10 more or 10 less**, only the **tens** digit changes.

When we find **100 more or 100 less**, only the **hundreds** digit changes.

$$74 - 10 = 64$$
$$764 + 100 = 864$$

Find 10 more or 10 less.

1. 64   +   10   =   ☐

2. 98   −   10   =   ☐

3. 34   −   ☐   =   24

4. 89   +   ☐   =   99

5. 88   −   ☐   =   78

Find 100 more or 100 less.

6. 634   +   100   =   ☐

7. 952   −   100   =   ☐

8. 170   +   ☐   =   270

9. ☐   +   100   =   736

10. ☐   −   100   =   53

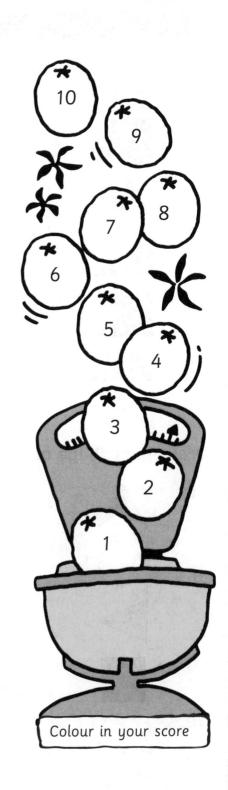

Colour in your score

Test 12 Addition

Here is a useful method when adding larger numbers.

When numbers get too large to use mental calculation strategies, you need another method. You can use a method known as a **formal written method** by setting out the calculations on paper and making sure you line the numbers in the correct place value columns (hundreds, tens and units).

$$
\begin{array}{r}
\text{HTU} \\
559 \\
+\ 262 \\
\hline
821 \\
\hline
{\scriptstyle 1\ 1}
\end{array}
$$

Do these on paper.

1. 314 + 62 =

2. 158 + 21 =

3. 828 + 33 =

4. 569 + 54 =

5. 729 + 59 =

6. 745 + 254 =

7. 554 + 369 =

8. 423 + 567 =

9. 653 + 378 =

10. 137 + 642 =

Colour in your score

10
9
8
7
6
5
4
3
2
1

Test 13 Word problems: multiplication and division

Learn these **multiplication** words:

multiply   TIMES   lots of   product   multiplication   multiple

Learn these **division** words:

factor   remainder   halve   SHARE   divide   division   quotient

Answer these questions.

1. What is the quotient of 20 and 5?

2. What is 2 multiplied by 9?

3. What is 60 shared by 10?

4. What is 10 times 8?

5. What is 20 divided by 2?

6. Liz has 10 pencils. Amy has half as many. How many pencils has Amy?

7. Arlo buys 8 tokens costing 5p each. How much money does he need?

8. Kim has 50p. How many 5p sweets can she buy?

9. Phil puts 8 stamps on each page. He has to fill 5 pages. How many stamps would he need?

10. Marco has 60p to share between his 6 friends. How much will each friend get?

Colour in your score

44

Test 14 3-D shapes

If you slice a **prism** into equal lengths all the slices are the **same shape and size**.

triangular prism	hexagonal prism	not a prism
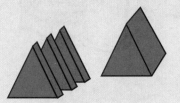	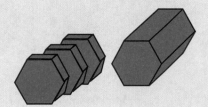	
All the slices will be the same.	All the slices will be the same.	All the slices will be different sizes.

Draw a line from each shape to where it goes on the diagram.

	prism	not a prism
1.		
2.		
3.		
4.		
5.		
6.		
7.		
8.		
9.		
10.		

Colour in your score

45

Test 15 Measures and time

You need to remember **equivalent** measurements.

1 m = 100 cm	1 l = 1000 ml	1 hour = 60 minutes
1 cm = 10 mm	1 kg = 1000 g	1 minute = 60 seconds
	1 km = 1000 m	

Answer these questions.

1. $\frac{3}{4}$ metre = ☐ cm

2. 2 kilograms = ☐ g

3. 2 kilometres = ☐ m

4. $\frac{1}{2}$ litre = ☐ ml

5. 2 cm = ☐ mm

6. $\frac{1}{2}$ hour = ☐ minutes

7. $\frac{3}{4}$ hour = ☐ minutes

8. $\frac{1}{4}$ hour = ☐ minutes

9. $\frac{1}{2}$ minute = ☐ seconds

10. $\frac{3}{4}$ minute = ☐ seconds

Colour in your score

Test 16 Number patterns

The **last digit** of a number will tell you whether it is odd or even.

If the ending is
1   3   5   7 or **9**
the number is

odd

If the ending is
0   2   4   6 or **8**
the number is

even

Continue these number patterns.

1.   601   611   621

2.   789   689   589

3.   28   38   48

4.   99   89   79

5.   355   455   555

Write each number correctly on the diagram.

6.   39

7.   345

8.   216

9.   572

10.   481

odd	not odd

Colour in your score

47

Test 17 Multiplication and division

Multiplying by 2 and doubling are the same.

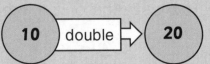

Dividing by 2 and halving are the same.

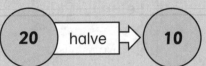

Doubling and halving are opposites.

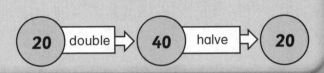

Double each of these.

1. 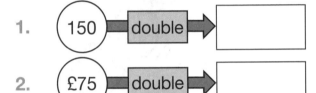 150 | double →

2. £75 | double →

3. 80 cm | double →

4. 120 m | double →

5. 15p | double →

Halve each of these.

6. 90 | halve →

7. £24 | halve →

8. 66 cm | halve →

9. 24 kg | halve →

10. 50p | halve →

Colour in your score

48

Test 18 Money (2)

When writing **money totals**, always put the pounds together and the pence separately, like this:

£1 + 20p + 20p + £2 +

10p = £3 and 50p

Remember 100p = £1 so 205p = £2 and 5p

Total these.

1. 20p ▸ 50p ▸ £1 ▸ [ ]

2. £1 ▸ 5p ▸ £1 ▸ [ ]

3. £2 ▸ £1 ▸ 10p ▸ [ ]

4. 50p ▸ 50p ▸ 1p ▸ [ ]

5. 2p ▸ 5p ▸ £2 ▸ [ ]

Write how many pennies are in these amounts.

6. £7 and 54p [ ]

7. £2 and 7p [ ]

8. £3 and 49p [ ]

9. £9 and 12p [ ]

10. £1 and 77p [ ]

Colour in your score

49

Test 19 Fractions (2)

$\frac{1}{3}$ of 15 **is the same as** 15 ÷ 3 = 5

Work out the answers.

1. $\frac{1}{4}$ of 12 =

2. $\frac{1}{2}$ of 28 =

3. $\frac{1}{3}$ of 18 =

4. $\frac{1}{5}$ of 20 =

5. $\frac{1}{4}$ of 16 =

6. $\frac{1}{10}$ of 60 =

7. $\frac{2}{3}$ of 24 =

8. $\frac{2}{5}$ of 35 =

9. $\frac{3}{4}$ of 32 =

10. $\frac{3}{10}$ of 90 =

Colour in your score

Test 20 Data (1)

We often write information in **lists** and **tables**.

The **order** and **position** of the information is important.

The order of lists can be things like: **alphabetical**, **size**, **date order**.

Tables have **columns** going down and **rows** going across.

	Road	Street	Avenue	Lane
Morris	✓			
Jenny		✓		
Ravi				✓
Sol			✓	

Where people live

Use the table above to answer these questions.

1. Who lives in a street? _____

2. Who lives in a lane? _____

3. Where does Morris live? _____

4. Where does Sol live? _____

5. Where does Ravi live? _____

Write the following lists in the columns below.

6. Peter, George and Lucy in alphabetical order.

7. April, February and November in date order.

8. 635g, 480g and 755g in order, starting with the lightest.

9. Lee, Sandra and Eric by word length, starting with the least number of letters.

10. 35 seconds, 1 minute and $\frac{1}{2}$ minute in order, starting with the shortest time.

6	7	8	9	10

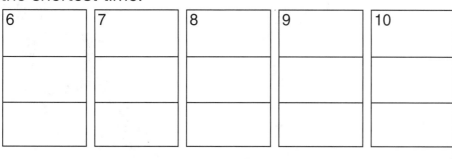

Colour in your score

Test 21 Telling the time with 12- and 24-hour clocks

When you write the time using the 12-hour digital clock you must always write **am** or **pm**. This is because the hands of a 12-hour clock go round twice in one day and you need to show which part of the day you mean.

The 24-hour clock uses numbers from 0 to 24 to stand for all the hours in the day. Always use four digits to write the time of the 24-hour clock.

00:00 (or 24:00) is midnight. After midday the hours become 13, 14, 15, etc (e.g. 6 pm is shown as 18:00).

For each clock face, write the time using the
12-hour digital clock.

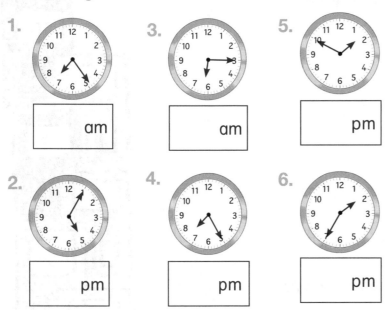

1. [ ] am

3. [ ] am

5. [ ] pm

2. [ ] pm

4. [ ] pm

6. [ ] pm

Match the 12-hour digital clock times to the correct
24-hour digital clock times.

12-hour digital clock	24-hour digital clock
7. 1.30 pm	09:45
8. 9.45 am	13:30
9. 6.15 pm	19:20
10. 7.20 pm	18:15

Colour in your score

52

Test 22 Subtraction

Here is a useful method for **subtracting** larger numbers.

When numbers get too large to use mental calculation strategies, you need to use a **formal written method**. Set out the calculations on paper and making sure you line up the numbers in the correct place value columns (hundreds, tens and units).

```
  H T U
  5⁴¹3
- 1 4 2
  3 7 1
```

Answer these using a formal written method.

1.   946   –   41   =   ☐

2.   595   –   64   =   ☐

3.   397   –   71   =   ☐

4.   671   –   79   =   ☐

5.   285   –   67   =   ☐

6.   691   –   327   =   ☐

7.   322   –   254   =   ☐

8.   573   –   494   =   ☐

9.   792   –   473   =   ☐

10.   573   –   166   =   ☐

Colour in your score

53

Test 23 Money problems

When adding several amounts, it sometimes helps to make a list, then total.

Remember 100p = £1

19p   40p   25p   54p   30p   48p   15p   24p

lolly	19p
ice-cream	25p
pizza	54p
total	98p

What is the total cost of the following?

1. 1 lolly, 1 hot dog, 1 ice-cream cone and 1 slice of pizza

2. 2 hot dogs and 2 slices of pizza

3. 1 ice-cream cone and 2 lollies

4. 1 ice-cream cone, 2 slices of pizza and 1 hot dog

5. 1 slice of pizza and 2 lollies

How much change from £1 would you have if you bought the following?

6. 3 bowls of ice-cream

7. 1 milkshake and 1 slice of pie

8. 1 slice of pie and 1 hamburger

9. 2 hamburgers

10. 1 bowl of ice-cream and 2 milkshakes

Colour in your score

Test 24 Shapes: right angles

A **right angle** is a $\frac{1}{4}$ of a whole turn.

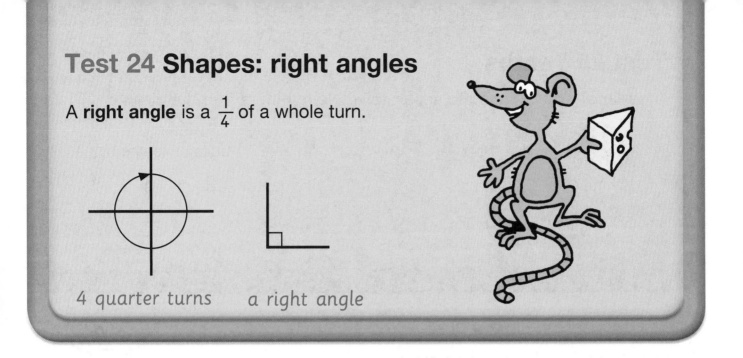

4 quarter turns   a right angle

Circle the right angles in the shapes below.

1.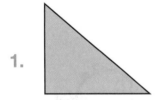

2.

3.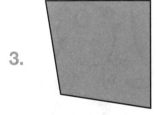

4.

5.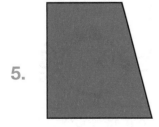

Tick the right angles and cross the angles that are not right angles.

6. 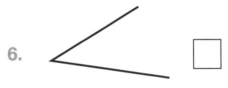 ☐

7.  ☐

8.  ☐

9.  ☐

10.  ☐

Colour in your score

55

Test 25 Tenths

A **decimal point** is used to separate whole numbers from fractions.

$$0.1 = \frac{1}{10} \qquad 0.2 = \frac{2}{10} \qquad 0.5 = \frac{1}{2}$$

units	tenths
2 ·	**6**
2	$\frac{6}{10}$

Change these fractions to decimals.

1. $\frac{7}{10}$ = [ ]

2. $1\frac{1}{2}$ = [ ]

3. $3\frac{3}{10}$ = [ ]

4. $\frac{9}{10}$ = [ ]

5. $2\frac{4}{10}$ = [ ]

Write the decimals on this number line.

6. [ ] 7. [ ] 8. [ ] 9. [ ] 10. [ ]

0 |—|—|—|—|—|—|—|—|—|—| 1

Colour in your score

56

Test 26 Division

Use multiplication to help work out **division** questions.

$24 \div 6 = \square$ ⇨ $6 \times \square = 24$

$6 \times 4 = 24$

⇩

$24 \div 6 = 4$

If a number cannot be divided exactly, it leaves a remainder.

$26 \div 4 = 6$ remainder 2

Answer these.

1. $30 \div 5 =$

2. $32 \div 4 =$

3. $42 \div 3 =$

4. $52 \div 2 =$

5. $85 \div 5 =$

Answer these and write the remainder.

6. $34 \div 4 =$ remainder

7. $29 \div 2 =$ remainder

8. $58 \div 5 =$ remainder

9. $47 \div 3 =$ remainder

10. $86 \div 10 =$ remainder

Colour in your score

57

Test 27 Problems

- When answering **word problems** you must read the words **carefully**.

- Decide whether it is an **add**, **subtract**, **multiply** or **divide** problem.

- Look at your answer and ask yourself if it seems a sensible answer to the problem.

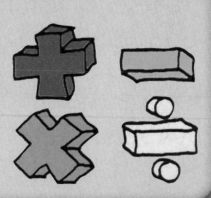

What time will it be half an hour after the times shown on these 12-hour clocks?

1. [   ]   2. [   ]   3. [   ]

4. [   ]   5. [   ]

6. The time is 6.25. How many minutes until 7.00?

7. The paper bill comes to £2 and 2p. How much change will there be from £5?

8. If 6 bread rolls cost £3 and 36p, how much does 1 roll cost?

9. Rebecca is 1 hour late for her swimming lesson. It is now 3.30 pm. What time should she have been there?

10. Carly had 35 conkers in each of her 2 pockets. How many conkers did she have altogether?

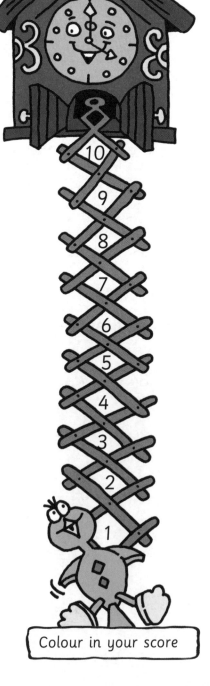

Colour in your score

Test 28 Multiplication

When **multiplying** it can help to break numbers up.

$$43 \times 5 =$$

$$40 \times 5 = 200$$
$$3 \times 5 = + 15$$
$$43 \times 5 = 215$$

```
    4 3
×     5
-------
  2 1 5
    1
```

Answer these.

1. 36 × 3 =

2. 41 × 4 =

3. 53 × 2 =

4. 47 × 3 =

5. 56 × 4 =

Answer these.

```
6.    5 3        7.    8 4        8.    6 7
    ×   3            ×   2            ×   4
    -----            -----            -----
```

```
9.    7 4       10.    5 9
    ×   3            ×   5
    -----            -----
```

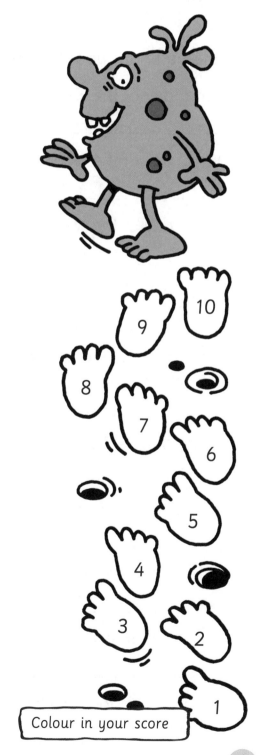

Colour in your score

Test 29 Time (2)

Calendars show us **months** and **days of the month**.

December						
Su	Mo	Tu	We	Th	Fr	Sa
				1	2	3
4	5	6	7	8	9	10
11	12	13	14	15	16	17
18	19	20	21	22	23	24
25	26	27	28	29	30	31

Use the calendar above to help you answer these.

1. What day of the week is the first day of December?

   _____

2. What day of the week was the last day of November?

   _____

3. What day of the week will the first day of January be?

   _____

4. How many Fridays are there in December?

   _____

5. How many Saturdays and Sundays are there altogether in December?

   _____

6. What date is 3 weeks after the 5th December?

   _____

7. What day of the week is the 25th December?

   _____

8. What date is 2 weeks before the 16th December?

   _____

9. What month is December in the year?

   _____

10. What month follows December?

   _____

Colour in your score

Test 30 Data (2)

On **picture graphs** the picture does not always show 1 of something.

It sometimes shows quantities such as **2, 5, 10** or **100**.

You have to look for the **key** to help you.

Key: **1 ball = 5 people**

Favourite ball games	
football	⚽⚽⚽⚽⚽
rugby	🏉🏉🏉
table tennis	⚪⚪
tennis	🎾🎾🎾🎾
basketball	🏀

Children were asked about their favourite ball games.

1. How many children chose football? ☐

2. How many children chose basketball? ☐

3. How many children chose tennis? ☐

4. How many children chose table tennis or rugby? ☐

5. How many children chose tennis or football? ☐

6. How many more children chose football than rugby? ☐

7. How many more children chose tennis than table tennis? ☐

8. Which game was most popular? —————

9. Which game was least popular? —————

10. How many children altogether were asked about their favourite ball game? ☐

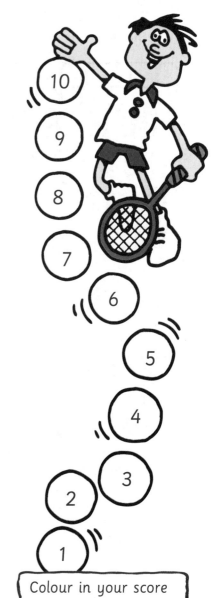

Colour in your score

61

ANSWERS

Page 2
a 33, 36, 39
b 36, 42, 48
c 36, 40, 44
d 60, 50, 40
e 55, 50, 45
f 104, 106, 108
2. a 78, 84, 90, 96
b 120, 130, 140, 150
c 24, 32, 40, 48, 56

Page 3
1. a 80
b 5
c 100, 3
d 10, 6
e 500, 50
f 300, 4
g 600 + 20 + 7
h 800 + 10 + 3
i 900 + 40 + 5
j 700 + 90 + 9
2. a 350   b 470   c 704

Page 4
1. a 12, 120, 1200
b 15, 150, 1500
c 15, 150, 1500
d 7, 70, 700
e 8, 80, 800
f 9, 90, 900
g 120
h 1300
i 1300
j 1800
k 240
l 40
m 1600

2.

Page 5
1. a 36   c 36   e 76
b 35   d 38   f 69

2. a 26 kg   c 60 kg   e 76 kg
b 28 kg   d 46 kg   f 77 kg

Page 6
1. a

triangles

b

pentagons

c

quadrilaterals

d

hexagons

2.

Page 7
1. a 87 cm, 107 cm, 137 cm,
170 cm, 207 cm
b 225 ml, 272 ml, 275 ml,
308 ml, 340 ml
c £1 and 9p, £1 and 38p,
£1 and 70p, £1 and 95p,
£2 and 5p
d 525 m, 608 m, 610 m,
635 m, 802 m

2. a 19 and 16
b 48 and 42
c 63 and 36
d 215 and 206

Page 8
1. a May
b Saturday
c 14th
d 26th
e Friday
f Wednesday

Page 9
1. a

b

c

d

2. a 9   d 10   g 15
b 2   e 24   h 14
c 12   f 2

Page 10
1. a $4\frac{1}{2}$cm   d 7 cm
b $8\frac{1}{2}$cm   e $3\frac{1}{2}$cm
c $6\frac{1}{2}$cm   f 9 cm
2. Check your child's lines with
a ruler.

Page 11
1. a 20, 70, 80, 100, 30, 90
b 10, 35, 40, 30, 15, 45
c 4, 14, 16, 12, 6, 18
d 48, 28, 32, 44, 36, 64
e 48, 56, 55, 12, 24, 96
2. a D U N D E E
b E D I N B U R G H

Page 12
1. a 94
b 101
c 64
d 148
e 165
f 126
g 131
h 141
i 171
j 256
k 251
l 301
2. a 444
b 355
c 620
d 1001
e 754
f 810

Page 13
1. a
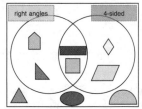

b
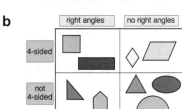

2. a D   b C   c A   d B   e A

Page 14
1. a 4 kg   c 9 kg   e 8 kg
b 7 kg   d 10 kg   f 13 kg
2. a 10   c 5   e 10
b 2   d 4

Page 15
1. a 50p, 20p, 10p coins
b £1, 10p, 5p coins
c £2, 50p, 5p coins
d £2, £1, 10p coins
e £1, 20p, 20p, 5p coins
f £1, 50p, 20p, 10p coins
g £2, 20p, 10p, 5p coins
h £2, £2, 50p, 5p coins
2. a Total 70p
50p, 10p, 10p coins
b Total £1 and 80p
£1, 50p, 20p, 10p coins

Page 16
1. a 14 cm   c 10 cm
b 14 cm   d 12 cm
2. a 16 cm   d 20 cm
b 14 cm   e 14 cm
c 20 cm

Page 17
1. a 80   d 41   g 270
b 16   e 13   h 350
c 40   f 25
2. a 50p, 15p, 35p or 40p,
35p, 25p
b 70p, 30p, 40p, 10p

Page 18

1. a 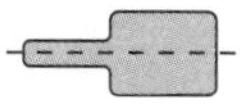 e 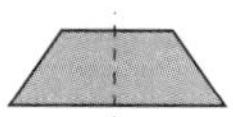
   b  f 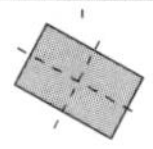
   c 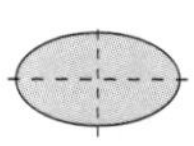 g 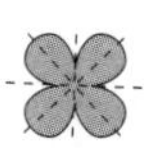
   d 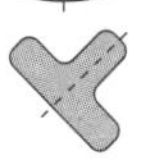 h 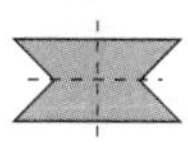
2. a  b 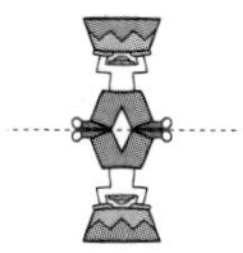

Page 19

1. a 60 ml c 90 ml e 800 ml
   b 20 ml d 500 ml f 400 ml
2. a 1000 ml d 100 ml
   b 500 ml e 5
   c 250 ml f 10

Page 20

1. a 6 remainder 1
   b 4 remainder 2
   c 5 remainder 2
   d 3 remainder 3
   e 3 remainder 1
   f 6 remainder 2
2. 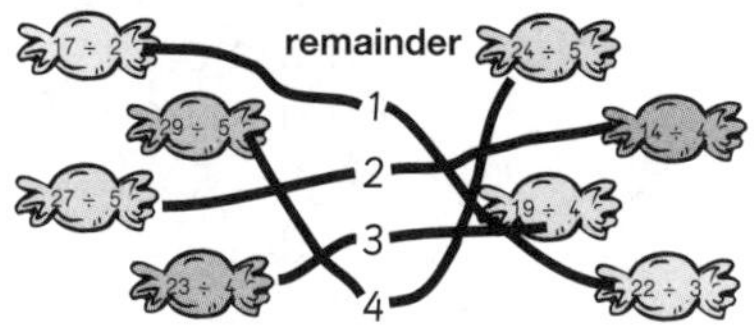

Page 21

1. a 5 faces, pyramid
   b 6 faces, cube
   c 5 faces, prism
   d 4 faces, pyramid
   e 6 faces, cuboid
   f 7 faces, prism
2.

	prism	not a prism
1 or more triangle faces	a c	b f
no triangle faces	d e	g

Page 22

1. a 80, 86, 85
   b 90, 93, 92
   c 100, 104, 103
   d 110, 115, 114
   e 110, 116, 115
   f 140, 144, 143
2. 51 → 49 41 → 59
   61 → 39 29 → 71
   69 → 31

Page 23

1. a 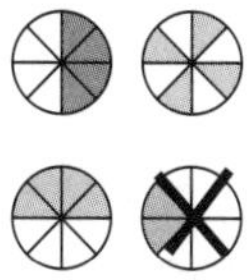 c 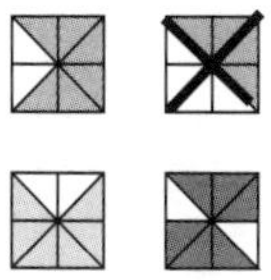
   b 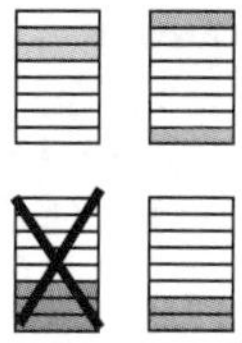
2. a $\frac{2}{6}$ and $\frac{1}{3}$ d $\frac{2}{8}$ and $\frac{1}{4}$
   b $\frac{4}{8}$ and $\frac{1}{2}$ e $\frac{3}{6}$ and $\frac{1}{2}$
   c $\frac{2}{4}$ and $\frac{1}{2}$ f $\frac{5}{10}$ and $\frac{1}{2}$

Page 24

1. $\frac{7}{7} = 1$
2. $\frac{3}{6} = \frac{1}{2}$
3. $\frac{3}{4}$
4. $\frac{10}{15} = \frac{2}{3}$
5. $\frac{5}{9}$
6. $\frac{12}{14} = \frac{6}{7}$
7. $\frac{3}{8}$
8. $\frac{1}{7}$
9. $\frac{6}{18} = \frac{1}{3}$
10. $\frac{6}{12} = \frac{1}{2}$

Page 25

1. a 12 e 18 i 26
   b 31 f 25 j 25
   c 43 g 26 k 19
   d 9 h 23 l 15
2. a
   8
   14 6
   26 12 18

   b
   3
   14 11
   21 7 18

   c
   8
   21 13
   27 6 19

   d
   9
   15 6
   18 3 9

Page 26

1. a 25p, 32p, 11p
   b 40p, 75p, 15p
   c £1 and 50p, £2 and 20p, £3 and 10p
2. a 80p b £9 and 80p
   c T-shirt and socks
   d £7 and 80p

Page 27

1. a 
   b 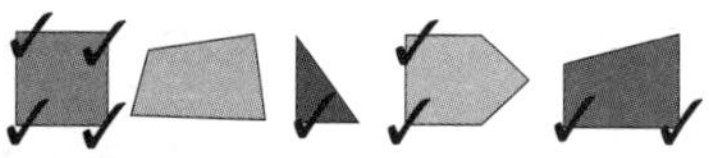
2. a west c east
   b south d west

Page 28

1. a 4.12 c 12.26
   b 10.38 d 5.34
   e  g 
   f  h 
2. a 35 minutes c 40 minutes
   b 40 minutes d 55 minutes

Page 29

1. a Joe d 4
   b 7 e Mark and Laura
   c 3

Page 30

1.

74	46	108	94	114	136	28	150	96
102	85	77	109	192	59	261	395	128
314	61	100	205	116	299	94	105	306
108	93	209	183	318	417	89	101	200
52	74	82	211	260	300	192	245	412
112	196	418	309	234	108	386	193	350
376	190	210	106	92	34	76	84	272

You can see the odd number 99

2. a 16 e 14 i 11
   b 8 f 16 j 19
   c 20 g 28 k 17
   d even h even l odd
   Answers **a–h** coloured blue
   Answers **i–l** coloured red

Page 31

1. 200 + 50 + 1, two hundred and fifty-one, 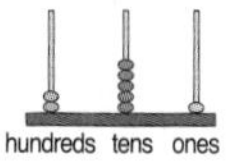

   736, seven hundred and thirty-six, 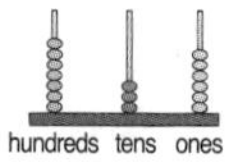

   464, 400 + 60 + 4, four hundred and sixty-four

   976, 900 + 70 + 6, 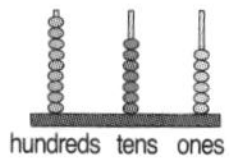

2. a 6
   b 346, 364, 436, 463, 634, 643

Page 32

1. 60
2. 660
3. 606
4. 16
5. 666
6. 3
7. 900
8. 0
9. 400
10. 9

Page 33

1. 110
2. 60
3. 80
4. 1400
5. 500
6. 1700
7. 1600
8. 90
9. 70
10. 1300

Page 34

1. 168
2. 274
3. 372
4. 242
5. 932
6. £1 and 20p
7. 40
8. 4
9. £1 and 74p
10. £2 and 90p

Page 35

1. hexagon
2. pentagon
3. quadrilateral
4. octagon
5. triangle
6. 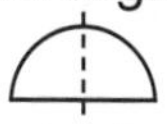
7. 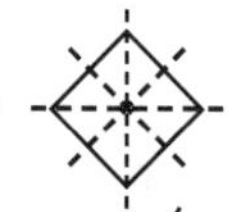
8. 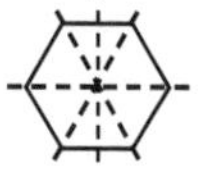
9. 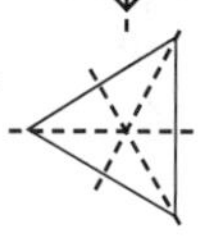
10. 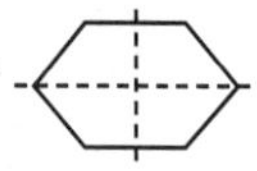

Page 36
1.	93	6.	952
2.	152	7.	401
3.	711	8.	808
4.	670	9.	1009
5.	419	10.	714

Page 37
1.	40	6.	33
2.	18	7.	40
3.	60	8.	14
4.	35	9.	45
5.	8	10.	48

Page 38
1. £10 and 15p
2. £15 and 30p
3. £30 and 55p
4. £20 and 65p
5. £12 and 50p
6. £5 and 50p
7. £2 and 25p
8. £1 and 20p
9. 75p
10. £12 and 50p

Page 39
1. $\frac{2}{6}$ and $\frac{1}{3}$
2. $\frac{4}{8}$ and $\frac{2}{4}$ or $\frac{1}{2}$
3. $\frac{4}{8}$ and $\frac{2}{4}$ or $\frac{1}{2}$
4. $\frac{2}{4}$ and $\frac{1}{2}$
5. $\frac{3}{9}$ and $\frac{1}{3}$
6. 8 squares coloured
7. 4 squares coloured
8. 14 squares coloured
9. 15 squares coloured
10. 2 squares coloured

Page 40
1. 30 minutes
2. 20 minutes
3. 15 minutes
4. 5 minutes
5. 3 hours
6.
7.
8.
9.
10.

Page 41
1.
2.
3.
4.
5.
6.
7.
8.
9.
10.

Page 42
1.	74	6.	734
2.	88	7.	852
3.	10	8.	100
4.	10	9.	636
5.	10	10.	153

Page 43
1.	376	6.	999
2.	179	7.	923
3.	861	8.	990
4.	623	9.	1031
5.	788	10.	779

Page 44
1.	4	6.	5
2.	18	7.	40p
3.	6	8.	10
4.	80	9.	40
5.	10	10.	10p

Page 45
1. prism
2. not a prism
3. not a prism
4. prism
5. prism
6. not a prism
7. prism
8. prism
9. prism
10. prism

Page 46
1. 75 cm
2. 2000 g
3. 2000 m
4. 500 ml
5. 20 mm
6. 30 minutes
7. 45 minutes
8. 15 minutes
9. 30 seconds
10. 45 seconds

Page 47
1. 631 641 651 661
2. 489 389 289 189
3. 58 68 78 88
4. 69 59 49 39
5. 655 755 855 955
6. odd
7. odd
8. not odd
9. not odd
10. odd

Page 48
1.	300	6.	45
2.	£150	7.	£12
3.	160 cm	8.	33 cm
4.	240 m	9.	12 kg
5.	30p	10.	25p

Page 49
1. £1 and 70p
2. £2 and 05p
3. £3 and 10p
4. £1 and 01p
5. £2 and 07p
6.	754p	9.	912p
7.	207p	10.	177p
8. 349p

Page 50
1.	3	6.	6
2.	14	7.	16
3.	6	8.	14
4.	4	9.	24
5.	4	10.	27

Page 51
1. Jenny
2. Ravi
3. Road
4. Avenue
5. Lane
6. George, Lucy, Peter
7. February, April, November
8. 480g 635g 755g
9. Lee, Eric, Sandra
10. $\frac{1}{2}$ minute
35 seconds
1 minute

Page 52
1. 7.24 am
2. 5.05 pm
3. 6.15 am
4. 7.25 pm
5. 1.50 pm
6. 1.35 am

7.
12-hour digital clock	24-hour digital clock

8–10.

Page 53
1.	905	6.	364
2.	531	7.	68
3.	326	8.	79
4.	592	9.	319
5.	218	10.	407

Page 54
1. £1 and 38p
2. £1 and 88p
3. 63p
4. £1 and 73p
5. 92p
6. 10p
7. 61p
8. 28p
9. 4p
10. 40p

Page 55
1.   2.
3.   4.
5.
6. not a right angle
7. right angle
8. right angle
9. not a right angle
10. not a right angle

Page 56
1.	0.7	6.	0.1
2.	1.5	7.	0.3
3.	3.3	8.	0.5
4.	0.9	9.	0.7
5.	2.4	10.	0.9

Page 57
1.	6	3.	14
2.	8	4.	26
5.	17		
6. 8 remainder 2
7. 14 remainder 1
8. 11 remainder 3
9. 15 remainder 2
10. 8 remainder 6

Page 58
1. 12.00
2. 8.45
3. 11.55
4. 1.15
5. 12.20
6. 35 minutes
7. £2 and 98p
8. 56p
9. 2.30 pm
10. 70

Page 59
1.	108	6.	159
2.	164	7.	168
3.	106	8.	268
4.	141	9.	222
5.	224	10.	295

Page 60
1. Thursday
2. Wednesday
3. Sunday
4. 5
5. 9
6. 26th December
7. Sunday
8. 2nd December
9. 12th
10. January

Page 61
1. 25
2. 5
3. 20
4. 25
5. 45
6. 10
7. 10
8. football
9. basketball
10. 75

English

Age 7-8

Contents

Activities

2   Word families
3   Spelling verbs
4   Speaking and listening (1)
5   Prefixes
6   Synonyms
7   Speech marks
8   Verbs
9   More verbs
10 Speaking and listening (2)
11 More about writing speech
12 *An* or *a*?
13 Suffixes *er* and *est*
14 Writing non-fiction: paragraphs
15 Words ending in *sure* and *ture*
16 Spellings that use *y* when they have an *i* sound

17 Spelling *ou*
18 Adding the suffix *ly* to an adjective to make an adverb
19 Alphabetical order
20 The suffix *cian*
21 Pronouns
22 Collective nouns
23 Commas
24 Homophones
25 Writing instructions
26 The suffix *ation*
27 Spelling *ei*, *eigh*, *ey*
28 The suffix *sion*
29 Singular and plural
30 Conjunctions
31 First and third person accounts

Quick Tests

32 Test 1 Prefixes
33 Test 2 Verbs
34 Test 3 Phonemes
35 Test 4 Comprehension (1)
36 Test 5 Punctuation marks
37 Test 6 Speech marks
38 Test 7 Alphabetical order
39 Test 8 Verbs: past tense
40 Test 9 Comprehension (2) – dialogue
41 Test 10 Comprehension (3) – instructions
42 Test 11 Comprehension (4) – inferring meaning
43 Test 12 Singular and plural
44 Test 13 Handwriting (1)
45 Test 14 Handwriting (2)

46 Test 15 Dictation
47 Test 16 Story writing (1) – settings
48 Test 17 Subject and verb agreement
49 Test 18 Collective nouns
50 Test 19 Story writing (2) – characters
51 Test 20 Story writing (3) – planning
52 Test 21 More prefixes
53 Test 22 Pronouns
54 Test 23 Using paragraphs in stories
55 Test 24 First and third person
56 Test 25 Conjunctions
57 Test 26 Playing with words
58 Test 27 Possessive pronouns
59 Test 28 Apostrophes
60 Test 29 More speech marks
61 Test 30 Evaluating and editing your work

62 Answers

Alison Head and Louis Fidge

Word families

Many **words belong** to word families. Being able to spell one word in the family can help you to spell the rest.

sp**oon**

m**oon**

ball**oon**

1 Put these words in their correct families. The first one has been done for you.

a light   d goat   g fright   j bright

b boat   e play   h tame   k hay

c name   f frame   i loan   l lay

ight	**oa**	**ame**	**ay**
light			
_____	_____	_____	_____
_____	_____	_____	_____
_____	_____	_____	_____

2 Write two more words for each of these word families.

a stain   lain   _____   _____

b allow   bow   _____   _____

c plate   grate   _____   _____

d sail   pail   _____   _____

e book   rook   _____   _____

f tear   near   _____   _____

g teach   preach   _____   _____

h spent   lent   _____   _____

i swell   fell   _____   _____

j hive   strive   _____   _____

2

Spelling verbs

When we add *ing* to a verb, we have to **take care** with spelling.

Several verbs ending in *e* (like *smile*) lose the *e* when we add *ing*.

Several verbs with a short vowel sound in the middle, like the *u* in *run*, double the final consonant.

Kate is smil**ing**.

Rob is ru**nn**ing.

1 Look at each verb. Then circle its correct *ing* spelling.

a	hope	hopping	hopeing	hoping
b	bake	bakeing	baking	bakking
c	clap	claping	clapeing	clapping
d	spin	spining	spineing	spinning
e	win	wining	winning	wineing
f	lose	losing	lossing	loseing
g	shut	shuting	shuteing	shutting
h	fit	fitting	fiteing	fiting
i	make	makeing	making	makking
j	swim	swimmming	swimming	swiming
k	slip	slipping	slipeing	sliping

2 Write these verbs with their correct *ing* spelling.

a ride + ing = _____

b plan + ing = _____

c sit + ing = _____

d shop + ing = _____

e stare + ing = _____

f jog + ing = _____

g slip + ing = _____

h hate + ing = _____

i rub + ing = _____

j hit + ing = _____

k raise + ing = _____

l shake + ing = _____

Speaking and listening (1)

Being able to speak clearly and listen carefully to others is very important. Interviewing someone helps to practise these skills.

1 Interview a friend about their favourite hobby. Perhaps they are in a sports team, or have a pet. You will need to ask some questions to find out information. Make sure you listen carefully to their answers.

Plan some questions you can ask. You do not need to write in full sentences as these are notes to help you to give a good interview.

a _____

b _____

c _____

d _____

e _____

2 Can you remember what your friend said? Write an account of what you remember in the box.

Prefixes

You can add prefixes to the **beginning** of some words to change their meanings.

happy

unhappy

Different prefixes mean different things.

un = not   *dis* = not   *re* = again   *pre* = before

1 Choose *un* or *dis* to make these words mean the opposite. Then write the new words.

a ___un___ + able   = ___unable___   f _____ + popular = _____

b _____ + seen   = _____   g _____ + do   = _____

c _____ + qualify   = _____   h _____ + appear   = _____

d _____ + usual   = _____   i _____ + own   = _____

e _____ + obey   = _____   j _____ + tidy   = _____

2 Write the correct prefix *un*, *dis*, *re* or *pre.* Then list the completed words in the correct boxes.

a _____well   d _____pare   g _____agree   j _____lucky

b _____cycle   e _____turn   h _____honest   k _____build

c _____allow   f _____kind   i _____dict   l _____vious

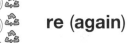

un (not)	**dis (not)**	**re (again)**	**pre (before)**
_____	_____	_____	_____
_____	_____	_____	_____
_____	_____	_____	_____

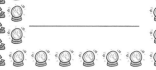

Synonyms

Synonyms are words that have **similar meanings**.

fast

speedy

quick

Choosing synonyms for words we use a lot can make our writing more interesting.

1 Write two synonyms from the box for each word.

> glum pleased huge tiny unhappy freezing small excellent
> after joyful brilliant large chilly unkind mean later

a big _____ _____   g sad _____ _____

b little _____ _____   h happy _____ _____

c good _____ _____

d cold _____ _____

e nasty _____ _____

f then _____ _____

2 Write a synonym for each of these words.

a run _____   g fast _____

b laugh _____   h old _____

c wet _____   i walk _____

d hungry _____   j closed _____

e speak _____   k begin _____

f seat _____   l simple _____

Speech marks

Speech marks, or 'inverted commas', show that someone is **speaking**. We write what the person says between the speech marks.

"Today is my birthday," said Jack.
Molly said, "Happy birthday."

1 Add speech marks at the end of the speech in these sentences. Take care to put them the right side of the comma. Use the examples above to help you.

a "My best friend is Max, said Joel.

b "I love football, said Rita.

c "We are going swimming today, said Mum.

d Martin said, "That is my bag.

e "I have a new puppy, said Alfie.

f The teacher said, "It is raining today.

g Dad shouted, "Do not forget your coat!

h "Let us watch TV, said Sophie.

2 Find the speech in these sentences and add the speech marks.

a I am going skating tomorrow, said Heather.

b Sarah said, That is not fair!

c Harry sighed, I love chocolate cake!

d I would like a drink please, said Lucy.

e Look at my new bike, said Katy.

f The bus driver called out, This is your stop!

g Time to tidy up, shouted Mrs Moors.

h Gran said, See you soon!

Verbs

Verbs tell us what a person or thing is **doing**.

A *fish* **swims**.

Choosing the right verb can also tell the reader exactly how a person or thing does something.

This *frog* **hops**.

This *frog* **leaps**.

1 Underline the verb in each sentence.

a The sun shines.

b Birds fly.

c Molly reads a book.

d Sam paints a picture.

e Chris watches television.

f Matthew waits for the train.

g Charlotte munches her lunch.

h The lorries turn a corner.

i He shuts the door.

j The school bell rings.

2 Write the verbs in the box next to the verb with similar meanings.

dash	slumber	see	build	peer	sprint
watch	jog	snooze	create	doze	assemble

run _____ _____ _____

make _____ _____ _____

sleep _____ _____ _____

look _____ _____ _____

More verbs

The **tense** of a verb tells us whether something is happening now or whether it has happened already.

I **am eating** the cake.

This is the **present tense**.

I **ate** the cake.

This is the **past tense**.

1 Underline the correct past tense verb to complete each sentence. The verbs are in **bold**.

a Rob **walks walked** home last night.

b Last year I **went goes** to France.

c My glass **is was** full before I drank my juice.

d Mum **fixed fixes** my bike this morning.

e Last Saturday we **bakes baked** a cake.

f Yesterday I **swaps swapped** a toy with Ben.

g Dad **drives drove** us to the party last Tuesday.

h Mum **hid hides** my presents before last Christmas.

i I **worry worried** before last week's test.

j Sally **tried tries** to catch the last bus yesterday.

2 Complete this chart by filling in the missing past and present verbs.

Present	Past		Present	Past
a give	_____		g _____	copied
b _____	tapped		h wash	_____
c _____	skipped		i speak	_____
d mix	_____		j _____	built
e bring	_____		k am	_____
f _____	caught		l _____	grew

Speaking and listening (2)

Giving oral (spoken) reports and presentations helps you to speak clearly and listen carefully.

1 You are going to give a presentation to a grown-up about your favourite book. Answer these questions to help you plan your presentation.

a What is the title of your favourite book? Who is the author?

_____

b Why is it your favourite? What do you love about the book?

_____

c Who is your favourite character, and why?

_____

d What, in your opinion, is the best thing that happens in the book?

_____

e How did the story end? Were the problems resolved?

_____

2 Plan an oral report on an event at school. It could be a play, sports day, fundraising event – you choose. Make notes to help you plan your report.

a What was the event?

_____

b Why was the event held?

_____

c Describe what happened at the event.

_____

d How did you feel about what happened?

_____

e Would you want to take part in a similar event if you got the chance? Give reasons for your answer.

_____

More about writing speech

When we write what someone says, we also need to write **who** is saying it.

We can say more about what the person is saying, like whether it is a question or a reply.

"My hat is blue,"
said Paul.

"Where did you get it?"
asked Alex.

"From the junkyard,"
replied Chris.

1 Circle the name of the person speaking in each sentence. Then underline the word that tells us more about what they are saying. The first one is done for you.

a "Stop it!" underline{shouted} (Jack).

b "Where is my book?" asked Sophie.

c "It is on your bed," answered Mum.

d "Shall we go out?" suggested Tim.

e "Good idea!" replied Ella.

f Jake grumbled, "My head hurts."

g Lucy asked, "What time is it?"

h Dad explained, "The toy is broken."

i Sally demanded, "Why can't I?"

j Mum replied, "Because it is late."

2 Underline the best word in bold to complete each sentence.

a "I am going out," **said asked** James.

b "Where are you going?" **explained asked** Chloe.

c "I need to post a letter," **demanded replied** James.

d "Could you post one for me?" **asked argued** Ryan.

e "Of course," **asked answered** James.

f "It is to my friend Asher," **requested explained** Ryan.

g "It is raining," **commented queried** Chloe.

h "No it's not," **questioned argued** James.

i "It is!" **giggled shouted** Chloe angrily.

j "I am going anyway," **insisted asked** James.

11

An or *a*?

The sound of a word's first letter shows you whether to say *a* or *an*. If the word starts with a vowel sound, use *an*. If it starts with a consonant sound, use *a*.

Be careful – it's about the way things **sound**. So you say '*an* hour' not '*a* hour'. *H* is a consonant, but in the word *hour* it makes a vowel sound. Say it out loud to check.

***an* apple**

***a* banana**

1 *An* or *a*? **Underline the correct word in bold in each sentence.**

a I can see **a an** herd of elephants.

b I'd like **a an** orange.

c Would you like **a an** drink?

d There's **a an** insect in my hair!

e Would you like **a an** cup of tea?

f I'm putting together **a an** album of photos for my nana.

g I'm making **a an** cheese sandwich.

h I'm getting **a an** cat next week.

2 **Underline the correct word in bold in these trickier sentences.**

a I need **a an** x-ray because I hurt my leg.

b I'm moving to **a an** house in the country this summer.

c I'll be ready in **a an** hour.

d **A An** UFO is an unidentified flying object.

e That has **a an** unknown answer.

f It is **a an** honour to be here.

g I'd like to be **a an** extra in a film.

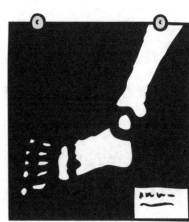

Suffixes *er* and *est*

We can make adjectives **tell us more** about the person or thing they are describing by adding letters such as *er* or *est*.

These groups of letters are called suffixes.

a big present   a bigg**er** present   the bigg**est** present

---

1 **Fill in the gaps. Look carefully at how the spelling changes when you add *er* or *est*.**

		Add *er*	**Add** *est*
a	quick	_____	quickest
b	long	longer	_____
c	nice	_____	nicest
d	_____	later	latest
e	hot	hotter	_____
f	fat	_____	fattest
g	_____	angrier	angriest

---

2 **Underline the *er* or *est* word in each sentence that is spelt wrong, then write it again correctly.**

a My jokes are much funnyer than Ben's, but Andy's are the funniest of all.

_____

b Ginny lives closer to the park than we do, but Sally lives the closeest of all.

_____

c I need a bigger pair of shoes, but even the bigest in the shop do not fit me.

_____

d Yesterday was sunier than Monday, but tomorrow is supposed to be the sunniest day so far this year.

_____

e I changed my picture to make the girl in it look happyer, but the boy has the happiest face.

_____

Writing non-fiction: paragraphs

Paragraphs (collections of sentences) can help make your writing interesting and **easier to understand**. They break writing up into sections.

In letters, paragraphs are used to introduce new ideas and points of view.

1 Put a mark to show where a new paragraph could start in this letter. One has been done for you. Use this example to help you.

I'm really enjoying my guitar lessons! My tutor is lovely, and he is teaching me lots of great songs. He has given me lots of chances to perform live, too. ‖Firstly, I have a chance to take part in a summer concert at the Sage, Gateshead – so exciting! Secondly, he has arranged for me to join in with a group who play for dances at The Irish Club in Newcastle. Finally, he asked if I could play with a group at an outdoor festival in Exhibition Park – and they said yes! As a result, I am practising every night, because I have so many new songs to learn. I'm quite busy.

2 Write a letter about something you have done recently. Use these connectives to help you organise your ideas into paragraphs.

a Firstly,

_____

b Secondly,

_____

c On the other hand,

_____

d Finally,

_____

e As a result,

_____

Words ending in *sure* and *ture*

Sure and *ture* are similar spelling patterns. Listen carefully when you say the words out loud and you will **hear** the difference.

trea**sure**

pic**ture**

1 These words all end in *sure*. Learn how to spell them using the LOOK, COVER, WRITE, CHECK method. Then write a sentence for each to show their meaning.

a sure _____

b pressure _____

c unsure _____

d measure _____

e pleasure _____

f treasure _____

g leisure _____

2 Now learn these spellings using the LOOK, COVER, WRITE, CHECK method. Then write a sentence for each to show their meaning.

a capture _____

b future _____

c creature _____

d culture _____

e lecture _____

f picture _____

g nature _____

Spellings that use *y* when they have an *i* sound

Sometimes *y* in a word makes an *i* sound. Read the word out loud and you can hear the *i* sound.

pyramid

1 Learn these spellings using the LOOK, COVER, WRITE, CHECK method.

a myth _____

b Egypt _____

c gym _____

d pyramid _____

e mystery _____

f hymn _____

g rhythm _____

h mysterious _____

i gymnastics _____

j mythical _____

Ask a grown-up to test you to see if you can remember the spellings.

2 Write a sentence for each of the words to show that you understand the meaning.

a mythical _____

b mystery _____

c hymn _____

d gym _____

e rhythm _____

f pyramid _____

Spelling *ou*

Sometimes, the *ou* blend of letters makes the short sound *u*. Say these words out loud to **hear the difference**.

mouth ➡ **ow** sound   youngster ➡ **u** sound

---

1 **Learn these spellings using the LOOK, COVER, WRITE, CHECK method.**

a young _____   g rough _____

b touch _____   h cousin _____

c double _____   i encourage _____

d trouble _____   j tough _____

e country _____   k enough _____

f youngster _____

Ask a grown-up to test you to see if you can remember the spellings.

2 **Write a sentence for each of the words to show that you understand the meaning.**

a double _____

b country _____

c encourage _____

d enough _____

e rough _____

f touch _____

Adding the suffix *ly* to an adjective to make an adverb

Many adjectives can be changed into adverbs by adding the suffix *ly*.

sad ➡ sad**ly**

1 Change these adjectives to adverbs by adding the suffix *ly*.

a glad ➡ _____

b sudden ➡ _____

c slow ➡ _____

d quick ➡ _____

e beautiful ➡ _____

f soft ➡ _____

g loud ➡ _____

h sharp ➡ _____

i quiet ➡ _____

2 Change these adverbs back to adjectives.

a thankfully ➡ _____

b perfectly ➡ _____

c slowly ➡ _____

d suddenly ➡ _____

e angrily ➡ _____

f beautifully ➡ _____

g gracefully ➡ _____

h quickly ➡ _____

i certainly ➡ _____

Alphabetical order

If a list of words all start with the same letter, we can use the next letter to put them in alphabetical order. This is useful when you are looking things up in a dictionary.

ball   bed

a comes before *e* in the alphabet, so *ball* comes before *bed*.

1 Write these names in alphabetical order.

Arthur	Ashley
Abigail	Amy
Anthony	Aiden
Alice	Attia

1 _____   5 _____

2 _____   6 _____

3 _____   7 _____

4 _____   8 _____

2 Look at the first two letters of each animal to help you find them in the alphabetical index. Then write down the page number.

a bats _____

b birds _____

c chickens _____

d ducks _____

e cows _____

f bees _____

g cats _____

h deer _____

i crows _____

j dogs _____

Animals	Page Number
bats	55
bees	12
birds	18
cats	50
chickens	33
cows	29
crows	82
deer	46
dogs	6
ducks	63

The suffix *cian*

The suffix *cian* makes the sound 'shun'. Say the word **out loud** to hear the sound.

magi**cian**

1 Learn these spellings using the LOOK, COVER, WRITE, CHECK method.

a musician _____

b electrician _____

c magician _____

d politician _____

e mathematician _____

f physician _____

g optician _____

h technician _____

Ask a grown-up to test you to see if you can remember your spellings.

2 Now write a sentence to show what each person does as a job.

a musician _____

b electrician _____

c magician _____

d politician _____

e mathematician _____

f physician _____

g optician _____

h technician _____

Pronouns

Pronouns can sometimes be used instead of nouns.

Tom likes **dogs**.   dogs = noun

Tom likes **them**.   them = pronoun

When you are talking about yourself, you use *I*, *me* or *my*.
These are all pronouns.

I like **my** dinner.

Aaron plays with **me**.

1) Underline the pronouns in these sentences. Look carefully as some sentences contain more than one!

a I ate my lunch.

b Will you be at school?

c I went to his party.

d Ali walked with them.

e We are going fishing.

f Ruby is my best friend.

g This game is mine.

h I played with her.

i Pete walks his dog.

j The boys did their homework.

2) Rewrite these sentences, replacing the bold nouns with a pronoun from the brackets.

a Emma opened **Emma's** presents. (his her their)

_____

b **The boys** gobbled their sandwiches. (We They You)

_____

c **Lucy** is my cousin. (He She It)

_____

d **My teacher and I** tidied the classroom. (We I They)

_____

e The king sat on **the king's** throne. (my their his)

_____

f **Mum and Dad** are going out tonight. (We They You)

_____

Collective nouns

Collective nouns describe **groups of things**.

A **herd** of elephants

A **pack** of wolves

These are collective nouns.

1 Pick a word from the box to complete these collective nouns.

a a flock of _____

b a swarm of _____

c a flight of _____

d a deck of _____

e a bunch of _____

f a litter of _____

g a pride of _____

h a gaggle of _____

i a troupe of _____

j a shoal of _____

cards
fish
sheep
monkeys
geese
stairs
bees
lions
puppies
flowers

2 Draw lines to match each thing on the left with their collective noun on the right.

a horses   pod

b birds   herd

c cars   group

d books   fleet

e musicians   library

f dolphins   flock

Commas

Commas tell readers when to **pause**.

Paul had tea, then he went home.

They also separate items in a **list**.

We bought apples, bananas, grapes and pears.

1 Look carefully at the commas in these sentences. Circle the commas in lists. Underline the commas which show a pause.

a Joe, my brother, is eight years old.

b For lunch, we had sausages, chips, peas and carrots.

c I'm wearing trousers, a shirt, socks and shoes.

d Actually, it is quite warm today.

e The bag split, so the shopping went everywhere.

f In stories, the knight always kills the dragon.

g You need sugar, flour, eggs and butter to bake a cake.

h Anyway, it was all fine in the end.

2 Add commas to these sentences. Read the words out loud to help you decide where the pauses or lists are.

a Mrs Smith my teacher marked my work.

b My best friends are Chris Sam and Jo.

c In the end I chose the blue coat.

d Although it was late we played one more game.

e Last night after Dad came home we watched TV.

f Alex my best friend lives next door.

g At the zoo we saw elephants lions camels and giraffes.

h Eventually I found the missing book.

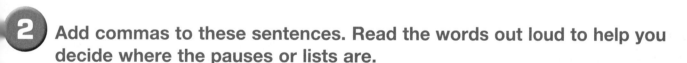

Homophones

Homophones are words that **sound the same** but have a **different meaning**. Sometimes they are also spelt the same way but have different meanings. Others are spelt differently but sound the same.

ball bawl

1 Choose the correct word to complete each sentence. Cross out the WRONG word.

a I am happy to **accept except** this award.

b What is the **affect effect** if I add salt to this ice?

c Catch this **ball bawl**!

d Pop a **berry bury** on top of each cake.

e Don't **brake break** that vase!

f I am going to the **fair fare** tonight.

g That's **grate great**!

2 Write a sentence for each word to show you understand what it means.

a groan _____

b grown _____

c here _____

d hear _____

e heel _____

f heal _____

g knot _____

h not _____

Writing instructions

Written instructions tell us **how to do** something.

To get to my house, turn right at the school gates. Then, turn left at the roundabout. I live at number 32.

Good instructions give us the important information in the right order.

---

1 Put these instructions for making a banana smoothie in the right order by numbering them 1–6.

a _____ Serve immediately.

b _____ Place banana in a blender with milk.

c _____ Pour into a chilled glass.

d _____ Ask an adult to blend the ingredients until smooth.

e _____ Peel one banana.

f _____ Add one scoop of vanilla ice cream.

2 Write these instructions in the right order.

Use your finger or a pencil to make a hole about 3 cm deep. Cover with soil. Keep soil just damp until seedling appears. Fill the pot with soil, leaving a gap at the top. Drop a sunflower seed into the hole. Find a small flower pot.

a _____

b _____

c _____

d _____

e _____

f _____

The suffix *ation*

The suffix *ation* can be added to verbs to make nouns – clever!

inform inform**ation**

If the word you are adding *ation* to ends in *e*, drop the *e* before you add the suffix.

adore ador**ation**

1 Add the suffix *ation* to these words to make new words.

a inform   ➡️ _____

b adore   ➡️ _____

c prepare ➡️ _____

d admire ➡️ _____

e condense ➡️ _____

f stagnate ➡️ _____

2 Write a sentence to show what each word means. If you need help, use a dictionary.

a vegetation _____

b frustration _____

c agitation _____

d fascination _____

e dedication _____

f decoration _____

Spelling *ei, eigh, ey*

ei, eigh and *ey* can all **sound the same** in words, even though they use different letter strings.

sovereign

eight

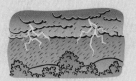

grey

1 Draw a line to match the words to their correct letter pattern.

a eight

b vein

c freight

d rein

e they

ei

eigh

ey

f obey

g sovereign

h weight

i prey

j grey

2 Underline the *ei, eigh* and *ey* words in these sentences.

a I weighed out a kilogram of apples.

b My dog obeys all my commands.

c I did a survey about which biscuits people like best.

d Father Christmas rides on a sleigh.

e That horse neighed at me!

f My neighbour is called Susan.

g They love swimming in the sea.

h Spiders have eight hairy legs.

i I can see rich veins of chocolate running through this ice cream – delicious!

The suffix *sion*

The suffix *sion* makes the sound 'shun'.
Say the word **out loud** to hear the sound.

television

1 Join each word to the correct description with a line.

a comprehension   Dividing something into smaller pieces

b division   Something to watch programmes on

c television   Being able to see

d discussion   Talking about something

e confusion   Finding something difficult to understand

f admission   Understanding something

g expression   Entrance fee; admitting something

h vision   A look on someone's face

2 Complete the words by adding *sion*. Then choose six of the words and write sentences to show you understand the meaning.

a inva_____

b pen_____

c mis_____

d ses_____

e ver_____

f expres_____

g ten_____

h occa_____

i pas_____

j permis_____

_____

_____

_____

_____

_____

_____

28

Singular and plural

When we change from singular to plural, sometimes the spellings change and sometimes the whole word changes. Sometimes the word stays exactly the same.

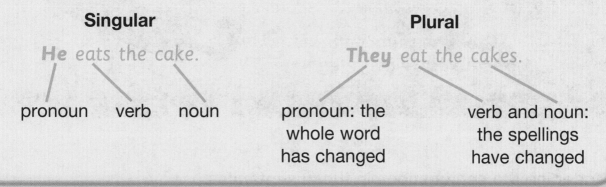

Singular	Plural
He eats the cake.	**They** eat the cakes.
pronoun verb noun	pronoun: the whole word has changed verb and noun: the spellings have changed

1 Fill in all the plurals. The first one has been done for you.

	Singular	Plural		Singular	Plural
a	he runs	_they run_	f	I walk	_____
b	she swims	_____	g	I eat	_____
c	I laugh	_____	h	she pushes	_____
d	he sleeps	_____	i	he wishes	_____
e	she builds	_____	j	I hope	_____

2 Write these sentences in the plural, making sure the nouns, verbs and pronouns are all plural.

a She picks the flower.

_____

b He kicks the ball.

_____

c I sharpen the pencil.

_____

d She washes the car.

_____

Conjunctions

Conjunctions are words that can **join** two short sentences together.

I took my umbrella.
It was raining.

I took my umbrella,
because it was raining.

1 Underline the conjunctions in these sentences.

a I turned the TV on when my favourite programme started.

b I did my homework, so I could go and play.

c I called for Asif, but he was out.

d Kelly likes bananas, but I like apples.

e I went to bed, because I was tired.

f I stayed at home, while Mum went shopping.

g Drew was just leaving when we arrived.

h I could wear my jeans or I could wear a skirt.

2 Choose a conjunction from the box to make the two short sentences into one sentence. Write each new sentence.

a I got a drink. I was thirsty.

_____

b Chris wants a skateboard. Mum said no.

_____

c Luke was three. I was born.

_____

d We waited. Dad packed up the car.

_____

e I could go bowling. I could go swimming.

_____

but

when

or

because

while

First and third person accounts

If I write about what I am doing, this is called a **first person** account.

I kicked the ball.

If **I** write about what someone else does, this is called a **third person** account.

Ella kicked the ball.

1 Read these sentences, then decide whether each one is a first person or third person account. Tick the correct box.

	First person	Third person
a Sean lost his bag.	☐	☐
b I had chicken pox.	☐	☐
c My cat is called Monty.	☐	☐
d They went to America on holiday.	☐	☐
e Dad missed the train.	☐	☐
f I live in a town.	☐	☐
g Lee and Kerry played football.	☐	☐
h I walk to school.	☐	☐

2 Read this third person account of life in the Handy family. Imagine you are Sarah Handy and rewrite it as a first person account.

The Handy family live in a small house in Bridge Street. They have a dog and a cat. Sarah Handy plays netball and is learning to play the violin. Her best friend is called Leah.

_____

_____

_____

_____

_____

_____

Test 1 Prefixes

A **prefix** is a group of letters we put **in front** of a word.
Prefixes **change the meaning** of the word.

well

unwell

Choose the prefix *un* or *dis* to complete each word.

1. _____pack

2. _____well

3. _____place

4. _____trust

5. _____fair

6. _____happy

7. _____agree

8. _____may

9. _____load

10. _____bolt

11. _____honest

12. _____do

13. _____arm

14. _____charge

15. _____please

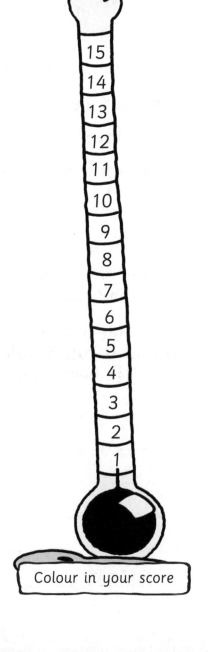

15
14
13
12
11
10
9
8
7
6
5
4
3
2
1

Colour in your score

Test 2 Verbs

A **verb** tells us what someone **is doing** or what **is happening**.

Anna **is riding** her bike.

Choose the best verb to complete each sentence.

1. The rabbit _____ into the burrow. (disappeared/spoke)

2. The child _____ in a whisper. (spoke/chased)

3. The bull _____ the boy across the field. (drew/chased)

4. I _____ up all the mess. (brushed/groaned)

5. Abdi _____ a lovely picture. (painted/crashed)

6. Who is _____ at the door? (eating/knocking)

7. The girls were _____ lemonade. (drinking/painting)

8. The injured man _____ with pain. (turned/groaned)

9. The lady was _____ a pram. (raining/pushing)

10. The sun is _____ in the sky. (shining/shouting)

11. A lion _____ loudly. (smiled/roared)

12. The car _____ into the wall. (crashed/crushed)

13. The dragon _____ its wings. (flagged/flapped)

14. The frog _____ onto the log. (hoped/hopped)

15. A letter _____ through the letter box. (came/screamed)

15
14
13
12
11
10
9
8
7
6
5
4
3
2
1

Colour in your score

Test 3 **Phonemes**

A **phoneme** is the **smallest unit of sound**. A phoneme may be made up of **one or more letters** which make **one sound**.

b + oa + t = boat

This word is made by using **three phonemes**.

Choose the correct phoneme to complete each word.

1. m_____n (oo/ir)

2. tr_____t (ee/ea)

3. gr_____ (ow/oo)

4. gl_____ (ue/oo)

5. r_____d (oa/ow)

6. cl_____ (aw/ow)

7. p_____nt (au/ai)

8. b_____n (ir/ur)

9. _____l (ay/ow)

10. th_____sty (oo/ir)

11. yesterd_____ (ai/ay)

12. narr_____ (ow/aw)

13. r_____nd (ow/ou)

14. s_____cer (ou/au)

15. b_____l (oi/oa)

Colour in your score

Test 4 Comprehension (1)

Comprehension exercises check that you understand the things you have read.

Read the text and answer the questions.

The dragon stretched out her purple wings, and yawned. A puff of smoke burst out of her nostrils, and a flame licked out of her mouth. She flexed one strong, scaly leg, then another. Her black claws clacked on the stone.

She stood up, and looked happily at her nest. Three green eggs lay there, rocking backwards and forwards. A chirping noise got louder and then there was a loud crack. One of the eggs split open, and a tiny head popped out. The other eggs opened and soon three little dragons were nestling down in their bed. The mother dragon stroked them with her paws, and sang them to sleep.

1. What colour were the dragon's wings? _____

2. What came out of the dragon's nostrils? _____

3. What came out of the dragon's mouth? _____

4. What were the dragon's legs like? _____

5. What colour were her claws? _____

6. What was in the nest? _____

7. What noise did the baby dragons make? _____

8. How many babies were there? _____

9. Once all the babies hatched, what did the mother dragon do? _____

10. How do you think the mother dragon felt?

_____

Colour in your score

Test 5 Punctuation marks

Punctuation marks make writing **easier to read**.

Most sentences end
with a **full stop**.

This is
an alien.

If it is a **question**, a
question mark is needed.

What is
this?

We put an **exclamation mark** when
we **feel strongly** about something.

What a
strange alien!

Put in the missing punctuation mark in each sentence.

1. Where do you come from

2. What a funny name

3. The spaceship landed

4. A door opened slowly

5. Run for your life

6. Who is there

7. What do you want

8. It's not fair

9. This is terrible

10. The sun set in the sky

11. The bees buzzed near the flowers

12. How did the car crash

13. When did the letter come

14. Stop that at once

15. We have sausages and chips for tea

Colour in your score

Test 6 Speech marks

When we write down what people say we use **speech marks**.

The **words the person says** go **inside** the speech marks.

The lumberjack said, "I cut down trees."

Fill in the missing speech marks.

1. Little Bo Peep said, I've lost my sheep.

2. The mouse said, I ran up the clock.

3. Humpty Dumpty said, I fell off the wall.

4. Incy Wincy Spider said, I climbed up the water spout.

5. Little Jack Horner said, I sat in the corner.

6. I marched up the hill, said the grand old Duke of York.

7. I went to London, said Dick Whittington.

8. I met a wolf, said Little Red Riding Hood.

9. I climbed a beanstalk, said Jack.

10. I ran away, said the gingerbread man.

11. Hansel said, I got lost in a wood.

12. I went to the ball, Cinderella said.

13. Old King Cole said, I'm a merry old soul.

14. I made some tarts, said the Queen of Hearts.

15. I'm very ugly, the troll said.

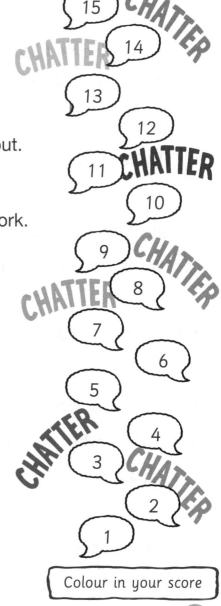

Colour in your score

37

Test 7 Alphabetical order

Many books are arranged in **alphabetical order**.

anteater **b**ear **c**amel

These words are arranged in alphabetical order according to their **first** letter.

deer **d**og **d**uck

These words are arranged in alphabetical order according to their **second** letter.

Order these words according to their first letter.

1. bat dog cat   _____

2. goat elephant fox   _____

3. hen kangaroo jaguar   _____

4. ostrich monkey lion   _____

5. rat seal penguin   _____

6. zebra swan panda   _____

7. hamster mouse donkey beetle _____

8. ox worm donkey giraffe   _____

Order these words according to their second letter.

9. crab cow cat   _____

10. bird bull bear   _____

11. parrot pike pelican   _____

12. shark sardine snake   _____

13. trout tiger turtle toad   _____

14. giraffe gnu goat gerbil   _____

15. bee badger bird buffalo _____

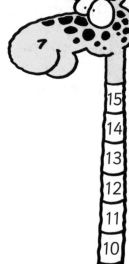

15
14
13
12
11
10
9
8
7
6
5
4
3
2
1

Colour in your score

38

Test 8 Verbs: past tense

I **am riding** my bike.

Yesterday I **rode** a horse.

This is happening **now**, so the verb is in the **present tense**.

This happened in the **past**, so the verb is in the **past tense**.

Join up each verb with its past tense.

1.	walk	hopped
2.	hop	moved
3.	carry	copied
4.	move	walked
5.	arrive	held
6.	beg	carried
7.	copy	spoke
8.	hold	wrote
9.	bring	came
10.	see	taught
11.	speak	arrived
12.	take	brought
13.	teach	took
14.	write	begged
15.	come	saw

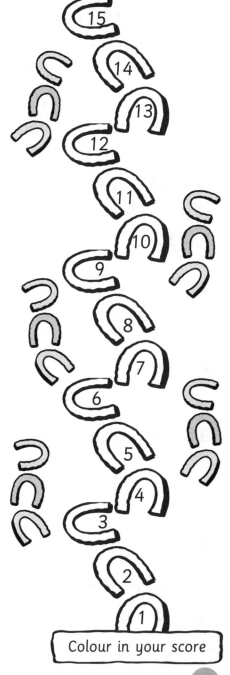

Colour in your score

Test 9 Comprehension (2) – dialogue

It is important that you understand what
is meant by words written in the dialogue
that you read.

Read the dialogue and answer the questions.

"What do you want to be when you grow up?"

"I'm not sure, Mum. Maybe a doctor ... or an astronaut ... or a vet."

"That sounds exciting! I used to want to be a teacher when I was a girl.
I wanted to be a mummy, too."

"Well, you are a mummy. But I didn't know you ever wanted to be a teacher.
Why didn't you do that?"

"When I was at university, I started volunteering at a centre for homeless
people. I saw that lots of people needed help, and I really enjoyed what
I was doing. When I left university, I got a job working with the charity
Shelter – and stayed there. I love my job!"

"That's brilliant. I hope I am as happy in the job I choose. In the
meantime, I'd better work hard at school."

1. Who is talking?

   _____

2. What does the child say they might like to do as a job?

   _____

3. Why did the mother not become a teacher?

   _____

   _____

4. Does the mother enjoy her job?

   _____

5. What does the daughter say she needs to do at school?

   _____

5

4

3

2

1

Colour in your score

40

Test 10 Comprehension (3) – instructions

Instructions tell you how to do things. It is important
that you understand what you read.

Read the instructions for making a monster mask and answer the questions.

What to do:	What you need:
1. Draw your monster design on the card.	Card
2. Cut the shape out.	Masking tape
3. With a grown-up, cut out eye and mouth holes.	Paints
	Scissors
4. Paint the mask and leave it to dry.	Glitter glue
5. Add details with markers and glitter glue.	Thick markers
6. Tape a piece of elastic to the back of the mask so you can wear it!	Elastic

1. What materials do you need for making the mask?

   _____

   _____

2. What do you do first?

   _____

3. What can a grown-up help you to do?

   _____

4. What do you need to do after you paint your mask?

   _____

5. What do you use to add details to your mask?

   _____

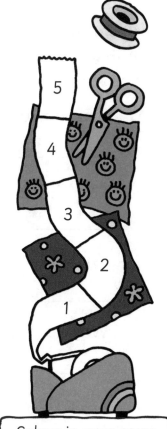

Colour in your score

Test 11 Comprehension (4) – inferring meaning

Open-ended questions do not
have one 'right' or 'wrong' answer.
You need to **infer** the answer.

Read the text and answer the questions.

The girl looked up at the sky. The moonlight fell like a silver veil, touching the garden and lighting everything with a silver glow. She listened carefully, her head on one side. Was that an owl, or something magical?

Suddenly, the bushes started to rustle. A snuffling noise began, and the girl stepped backwards. She moved nearer to the door, and called her dog closer. Whatever was in there? Her breath came faster and made white clouds in the cold air. The dog started to growl, and showed her teeth.

First a small pointed nose and then a prickly head poked out of the undergrowth. "It's a hedgehog!" the girl laughed. She stroked the dog and put her inside, before coming back to watch a hedgehog and her babies bumble around the garden, rummaging among stones and leaves.

1. How do you think the girl felt when she was listening to the owl?

_____

2. How do you think the girl felt when the bushes started to move?

_____

3. Why do you think the girl's breathing got faster?

_____

4. Why do you think the dog was growling?

_____

5. What do you think the hedgehogs were looking for?

_____

⑤ ④ ③ ② ①

Colour in your score

Test 12 Singular and plural

A noun may be **singular** (when there is **only one** thing).

A noun may be **plural** (when there is **more** than one thing).

one bus (singular)   two buses (plural)

Complete these phrases.
Be careful with some of the spellings!

1. one chair, lots of _____

2. one fox, lots of _____

3. one coach, lots of _____

4. one bush, lots of _____

5. one glass, lots of _____

6. one berry, lots of _____

7. one child, lots of _____

8. one man, lots of _____

9. one _____, lots of bikes

10. one _____, lots of boxes

11. one _____, lots of bunches

12. one _____, lots of dishes

13. one _____, lots of copies

14. one _____, lots of lorries

15. one _____, lots of sheep

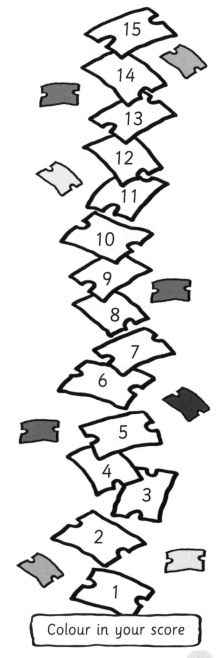

Colour in your score

Test 13 Handwriting (1)

Neat handwriting helps people to be able to read your work easily.

Write out these sentences in your best joined-up handwriting. Pay special attention to the shapes of the letters, and the way they are spaced out.

1. Today is my eighth birthday.

   _____

2. I got a bicycle from Mum and Dad.

   _____

3. Grandpa bought me a swing for the garden.

   _____

4. Mum made me a dinosaur cake.

   _____

5. There is also some amazing ice cream.

   _____

6. I can't wait to blow out the candles!

   _____

7. My friends are coming on Saturday for a party.

   _____

8. Dad has organised a treasure hunt.

   _____

9. He has bought real fossils as prizes.

   _____

10. He is going to bury them in the sandpit!

    _____

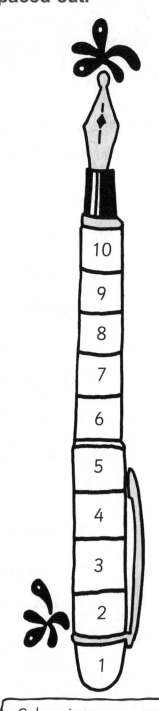

10
9
8
7
6
5
4
3
2
1

Colour in your score

Test 14 Handwriting (2)

When your handwriting is neat it makes people want to read what you have written!

Write out these sentences in your best joined-up handwriting. Pay special attention to the shapes of the letters, and the way they are spaced out.

1. I like gardening with Nana.

    _____

2. She has given me a bed of my own.

    _____

3. I have planted some yellow pumpkin seeds.

    _____

4. I painted a Halloween pumpkin on a label.

    _____

5. Instead of buying a pumpkin, I am growing my own!

    _____

6. I have planted some gourds too.

    _____

7. Gourds have bumpy, stripy skin.

    _____

8. I can't wait to make a Halloween display!

    _____

9. Nana will show me how to make pumpkin pie.

    _____

10. I bet it tastes wonderful!

    _____

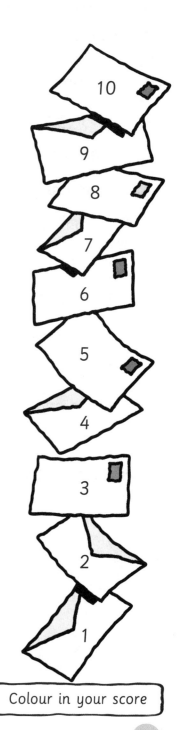

Colour in your score

Test 15 Dictation

Dictation is a really useful skill. It means listening when someone speaks, and writing down what they say. It is very useful for students taking notes, and many people use it as part of their jobs.

Ask a grown-up to read these sentences out loud, and write them down on a piece of paper.

1. My hamster is called Fred.

2. He is ginger and white.

3. He likes to eat sunflower seeds.

4. Fred has a wheel to play in.

5. He has a little house in his cage.

6. I fill it with soft bedding.

7. He needs fresh water every day.

8. I like holding Fred and letting him run up my arm.

9. He likes to play by running through big kitchen roll tubes.

10. I love my hamster very much.

How did you do?

Colour in your score

Test 16 Story writing (1) – settings

Settings – the places where your story happens – are important as they set the scene for the action.

Write a story about an adventure. Where – and when – does the action take place? Is it in the past or the future?

1. When is your story set?

    _____

2. Are there any cities? What do they look like?

    _____

3. What does the countryside look like?

    _____

4. What is the vegetation like?

    _____

5. Are there any animals?

    _____

6. What is the weather like?

    _____

7. What transport is there?

    _____

8. What do buildings look like?

    _____

9. What technology can you see?

    _____

10. What do the streets look like in the towns?

    _____

Colour in your score

Test 17 Subject and verb agreement

The **subject** (the main person or thing) and the **verb** in each sentence must **agree**.

The birds is flying. ☒

The birds are flying. ☑

Choose the correct form of the verb for each sentence.

1. Bells _____. (ring/rings)

2. The wind _____. (blow/blows)

3. A door _____. (open/opens)

4. Aeroplanes _____. (fly/flies)

5. An owl _____. (hoot/hoots)

6. Chickens _____ eggs. (lay/lays)

7. A rabbit _____ in a burrow. (live/lives)

8. Wolves _____. (howl/howls)

9. Mice _____. (squeak/squeaks)

10. I _____ my dinner. (eat/eats)

11. The children _____ to school. (go/goes)

12. Ben _____ a cold. (have/has)

13. The lady _____ some bread. (buy/buys)

14. Frogs _____. (hop/hops)

15. A cow _____ us milk. (give/gives)

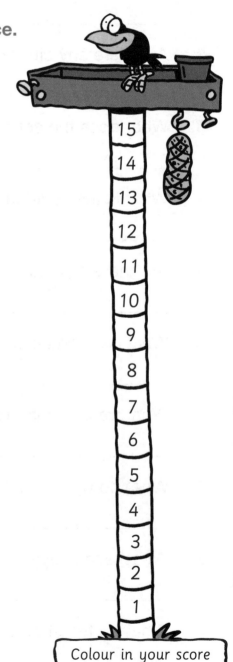

15
14
13
12
11
10
9
8
7
6
5
4
3
2
1

Colour in your score

Test 18 Collective nouns

A **collective noun** is the name given to a **group** of things.

*a **herd** of cows*

bunch   pile   library   flock   swarm
chest   shoal   fleet

Choose the best collective noun to complete each phrase.

1. a _____ of matches

2. a _____ of sheep

3. a _____ of bees

4. a _____ of drawers

5. a _____ of ships

6. a _____ of fish

7. a _____ of flowers

8. a _____ of books

sticks   stones   singers   athletes
soldiers   trees   bananas

Choose the best word to complete each phrase.

9. a choir of _____

10. an army of _____

11. a team of _____

12. a forest of _____

13. a bunch of _____

14. a bundle of _____

15. a pile of _____

Colour in your score

49

Test 19 Story writing (2) – characters

Characters are very important in any story.
If people don't care about the characters
in a story, they won't really care what
happens!

Use these questions to create a strong protagonist – the main character
in your story – for the story setting you planned on page 47.

1.   What does your character look like? (tall/short)

     _____

2.   How does your character dress? Describe their style of clothing.

     _____

3.   What is their hair like? Do they have a special style or colour?

     _____

4.   What does your character's face tell you about how they might act?

     _____

5.   Does your character have an unusual voice?

     _____

6.   How does your character act? Do they have any special skills or
     talents?

     _____

7.   Does your character have a job, or are they studying?

     _____

8.   Does your character have any transport?

     _____

9.   Does your character have any brothers or sisters?

     _____

10. Does your character have any hobbies?

     _____

Colour in your score

Test 20 Story writing (3) – planning

Planning a story is great fun – you get to decide what happens! Making a few notes about plot before you start writing your story can help to keep your story on track and moving forward.

Make notes in the boxes to plot and plan the story you created settings and characters for on pages 47 and 50.

1. Story opening – *make it exciting to make the reader want to read on.*

2. Build up – *what is the problem or challenge that needs to be overcome in your story?*

3. Main events – *what happens in your story?*

4. Who will overcome the problem, and how?

5. Conclusion – *how does your story end? Are all the problems solved?*

Colour in your score

Test 21 More prefixes

A **prefix** is a **group of letters** we put in front of a word.
Prefixes **change the meaning** of the word.

behave   **mis**behave

Choose the prefix *re* or *pre* to begin each word.

1. _____turn

5. _____caution

2. _____heat

6. _____mind

3. _____fix

7. _____fill

4. _____pare

8. _____fund

Choose the prefix *mis* or *ex* to begin each word.

9. _____judge

13. _____lead

10. _____handle

14. _____plode

11. _____port

15. _____pand

12. _____spell

Colour in your score

52

Test 22 Pronouns

A **pronoun** is a word that takes the place of a **noun**.

Ben cried when Ben hurt his leg.   Ben cried when **he** hurt his leg.

Choose the best pronoun to complete each sentence.

1. The lady went in the shop. _____ bought some apples. (He/She)

2. _____ am always busy. (We/I)

3. The boy shouted when _____ scored a goal. (he/it)

4. "Why are _____ late?" Mr Shah asked Abdi. (you/he)

5. "_____ are going to the park," the children said. (We/It)

6. _____ is a lovely day. (It/You)

7. Are _____ good at writing? (he/you)

8. _____ like playing games. (We/It)

9. The girl fell off her bike when _____ crashed. (she/you)

10. When the dog stopped _____ barked. (it/they)

11. The prince got up. _____ got dressed. (She/He)

12. I tried to lift the box but _____ was too heavy. (we/it)

13. When I shouted at the birds _____ flew away. (it/they)

14. The boy walked with the girl. _____ went into the park. (We/They)

15. When the man stopped _____ sat down. (you/he)

Colour in your score

Test 23 Using paragraphs in stories

Paragraphs help you to structure your story and interest your reader. When you are planning your story, it helps to plan some paragraphs.

Ideas for things to include in paragraphs will help you to write an exciting, well-structured story. Don't forget, you can also use new paragraphs to move between time and show flashbacks – and they are used in dialogue to show a new speaker.

Plan a story by writing notes for these paragraphs.

1. [   ] Introduction

2. [   ] Introduce main character

3. [   ] Introduce theme of the story

4. [   ] Introduce problem to be solved

5. [   ] Build-up of excitement

6. [   ] Develop other characters

7. [   ] Add suspense or change mood

8. [   ] Story climax

9. [   ] Resolution of problem

10. [   ] Strong final paragraph

STORY

~~~~~. 10
~~~~~ 9
~~~~ 8
~~~~~ 7
~~ 6
~~~~, 5
~~~ 4
~~~ 3
~~~~ 2
~~~ 1

Colour in your score

Test 24 First and third person

When we are writing about **ourselves** we write in the **first person**. We use pronouns like *I* and *we*.

When we are writing about **others** we write in the **third person**. We use pronouns like *he, she, it* and *they*.

I called for Ben.
We went swimming.

Annie and Lucy were surprised when **they** opened the box.

Say if each of the pronouns marked in bold is in the first or third person.

1. **I** went to school. _____

2. Tom went out when **he** finished washing up. _____

3. The children chattered as **they** ate the bananas. _____

4. When the dog appeared, **it** ran straight home. _____

5. The flowers looked lovely. **They** were all different colours. _____

6. **We** went to the cinema in the evening. _____

7. May **I** have some, please? _____

8. "**We** can do it!" Tom and Ben shouted. _____

9. The machine made a loud noise when **it** was turned on. _____

10. **I** am older than Sam. _____

11. Mr Shah went to bed. **He** went straight to sleep. _____

12. The lady was happy but **she** didn't smile. _____

13. **They** ran for the bus. _____

14. **I** was too frightened to move. _____

15. **We** all like to win games. _____

15
14
13
12
11
10
9
8
7
6
5
4
3
2
1

Push

Colour in your score

Test 25 Conjunctions

A **conjunction** is a **joining word**. It may be used to join **two sentences**.

I picked up the comic. I read it.   I picked up the comic **and** read it.

Choose the best conjunction to complete each sentence.

1. I had a bath _____ went to bed. (and/but)

2. An elephant is huge _____ an ant is small. (and/but)

3. I made a sandwich _____ ate it. (and/but)

4. Your towel is wet _____ mine is dry. (and/but)

5. A rabbit is fast _____ a snail is slow. (and/but)

6. I like swimming _____ playing rounders. (and/but)

7. You will get into trouble _____ you talk. (if/so)

8. I was wet _____ it was raining. (if/because)

9. It was hot _____ I took off my jumper. (so/because)

10. The door has been broken _____ I slammed it. (since/when)

11. I ran fast _____ I was late. (if/because)

12. We went for a walk _____ it was very hot. (so/although)

13. I will buy a lolly _____ you give me the money. (if/as)

14. You will get wet _____ you go in the rain. (if/so)

15. My uncle didn't come _____ I didn't see him. (so/if)

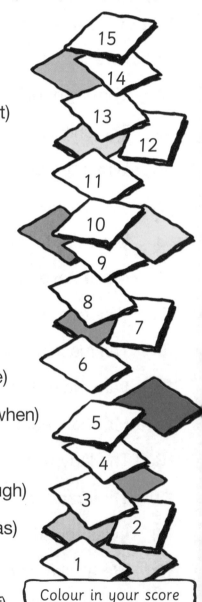

Colour in your score

56

Test 26 Playing with words

We can make new words by **changing** some letters.

fight   sight   bright   fright   slight

Make some new words.

1. Change the **f** in **f**arm to **ch**. _____

2. Change the **d** in **d**ead to **thr**. _____

3. Change the **w** in **w**ay to **del**. _____

4. Change the **f** in **f**eed to **gr**. _____

5. Change the **n** in **n**erve to **sw**. _____

6. Change the **n** in **n**ew to **scr**. _____

7. Change the **d** in **d**irt to **squ**. _____

8. Change the **m** in **m**oan to **gr**. _____

9. Change the **v** in **v**oice to **ch**. _____

10. Change the **w** in **w**ood to **bl**. _____

11. Change the **l** in **l**oud to **pr**. _____

12. Change the **m** in **m**ow to **borr**. _____

13. Change the **c** in **c**urb to **dist**. _____

14. Change the **d** in **d**are to **bew**. _____

15. Change the **n** in **n**ear to **app**. _____

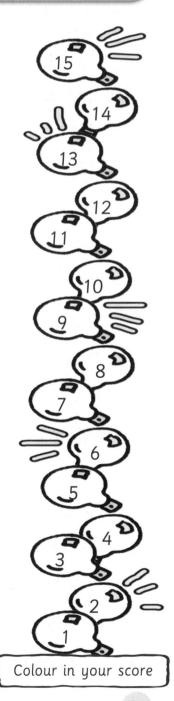

Colour in your score

57

Test 27 Possessive pronouns

Possessive pronouns tell us who the **owner** of something is.

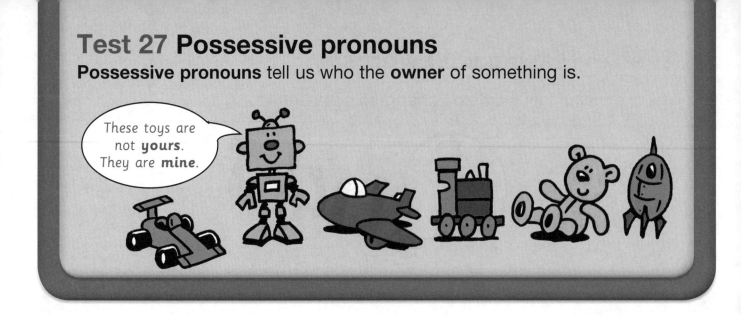

Some common possessive pronouns are:

mine	yours	his	hers
its	ours	theirs	

Underline the possessive pronoun in each sentence.

1. This book is mine.

2. This bag is blue – yours is red.

3. The boy was sure the pen was his.

4. Sam pointed to Anna and said, "This ruler is hers."

5. Rex belonged to the children – the dog was theirs.

6. "You can't have the ball. It's ours!" Tom and Ben shouted.

7. "The model Ali broke was ours!" Amy and Emma complained.

8. The girl picked up the purse – it was hers.

9. Mr Smith drove a sports car but it was not his.

10. I asked the lady if the pen was hers.

11. Go and look at the bikes. Mine is the silver one.

12. The children said, "These toys are ours!"

13. "I think these smelly socks are yours!" Mum said to John.

14. As soon as Ben won the race, he knew the prize was his!

15. This bag has your name in it so it must be yours.

Colour in your score

58

Test 28 Apostrophes

Sometimes we **shorten** words and leave letters out. These words are called **contractions**. We use an **apostrophe** to show where letters are missing.

I've got an ice cream.

I've = I have

Put in the missing apostrophes in the correct places in these contractions.

1. I m

2. h e s

3. I v e

4. w e d

5. I l l

6. w o u l d n t

7. w e r e

8. h e r e s

9. d o e s n t

10. i t s

11. w a s n t

12. w h o s

13. w o n t

14. d o n t

15. y o u r e

Colour in your score

59

Test 29 More speech marks

When we write down what people say we use **speech marks**, or 'inverted commas'.

The **words the person says** go **inside** the speech marks.

Emma said, "Do you like my pet spider?"

Put in the missing speech marks in these sentences.

1. Hello, Ben said.

2. It's nice to see you, Sam replied.

3. What a lovely day! exclaimed Ben.

4. Yes, it's so warm, Sam answered.

5. The weather forecast said it would rain, Ben said.

6. I don't think it will, Sam replied.

7. I can see a few black clouds, Ben commented.

8. I think they will pass over, Sam said.

9. Where are you off to? Ben asked.

10. I'm going to town to do some shopping, Sam answered.

11. May I come? Ben asked.

12. Yes, of course. Shall we walk or wait for a bus? Sam said.

13. Let's walk, Ben suggested.

14. I think I can feel a few spots of rain, Sam said.

15. Let's get the bus, then, said Ben.

Colour in your score

60

Test 30 Evaluating and editing your work

When you have written your story it is important to read things through to make sure everything makes sense. You can also use this time to add WOW words such as **shrieked** or **gasped**. WOW words can really help bring your story to life.

After you have evaluated your work, carry out a copy edit. This means you check the grammar, spelling and punctuation.

Go through the sentences and check that the spelling, punctuation and grammar are correct. Use a red pen to make your corrections.

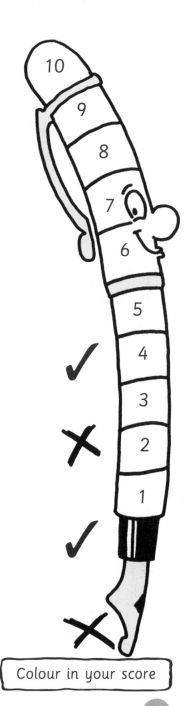

1. the ghost shimmered at the window. "A ghost!" shrieked Nora.

2. What do you mean, a ghost? Serena questioned.

3. "A see-through, wafting about, scary faced ghost!" shouted Nora

4. i think you are trying to trick me and its not even Halloween sighed Serena.

5. "I'm not. Look" nora shouted as she pointed up the stairs with a shaking hand.

6. Serena put her hands on her hips and said "Oh, OK … I'll play along."

7. She turned and looked behind her and screamed.

8. The ghost wiggled its fingers at her and shouted boo

9. "Its real!" she squealed and ran down the stairs to follow Nora.

10. "See, i told you i wasn't making it up." Laughed nora.

Colour in your score

61

ANSWERS

Page 2

1. ight light, fright, bright
  oa boat, goat, loan
  ame name, frame, tame
  ay play, hay, lay

2. Any words that follow the patterns given e.g. for a: main, pain, rain, vain etc

Page 3

1. a hoping
  b baking
  c clapping
  d spinning
  e winning
  f losing
  g shutting
  h fitting
  i making
  j swimming
  k slipping

2. a riding
  b planning
  c sitting
  d shopping
  e staring
  f jogging
  g slipping
  h hating
  i rubbing
  j hitting
  k raising
  l shaking

Page 4

1. Sensible questions about a favourite hobby.

2. An account of what their friend said, which should read well and make sense.

Page 5

1. a unable
  b unseen
  c disqualify
  d unusual
  e disobey
  f unpopular
  g undo
  h disappear
  i disown
  j untidy

2. un unwell, unkind, unlucky
  dis disallow, disagree, dishonest
  re recycle, return, rebuild
  pre prepare, predict, previous,

Page 6

1. a huge, large
  b tiny, small
  c excellent, brilliant
  d freezing, chilly
  e unkind, mean
  f after, later
  g glum, unhappy
  h pleased, joyful

2. Any sensible synonym for the words given

Page 7

1. a "My best friend is Max," said Joel.
  b "I love football," said Rita.
  c "We are going swimming today," said Mum.
  d Martin said, "That is my bag."

e "I have a new puppy," said Alfie.
  f The teacher said, "It is raining today."
  g Dad shouted, "Do not forget your coat!"
  h "Let us watch TV," said Sophie.

2. a "I am going skating tomorrow," said Heather.
  b Sarah said, "That is not fair!"
  c Harry sighed, "I love chocolate cake!"
  d "I would like a drink please," said Lucy.
  e "Look at my new bike," said Katy.
  f The bus driver called out, "This is your stop!"
  g "Time to tidy up," shouted Mrs Moors.
  h Gran said, "See you soon!"

Page 8

1. a shines
  b fly
  c reads
  d paints
  e watches
  f waits
  g munches
  h turn
  i shuts
  j rings

2. run dash, sprint, jog
  make build, create, assemble
  sleep slumber, snooze, doze
  look see, peer, watch

Page 9

1. a walked
  b went
  c was
  d fixed
  e baked
  f swapped
  g drove
  h hid
  i worried
  j tried

2. a gave
  b tap
  c skip
  d mixed
  e brought
  f catch
  g copy
  h washed
  i spoke
  j build
  k was
  l grow

Page 10

1. a The title and author of a book.
  b An explanation of why your child likes the book.
  c The name of a character and the reason for choosing them as favourite.
  d An explanation of the best thing that happens in the story.
  e Reasoned description of the end of the story and any story resolution.

2. Make sure your child can plan a report of an event successfully.
  a Name of an event.
  b Reason for holding the event.

c Description of what happened at the event.
  d Description of feelings after the event.
  e Opinion given on taking part in a similar event in the future, with reasons given.

Page 11

1. a "Stop it!" shouted Jack.
  b "Where is my book?" asked Sophie.
  c "It is on your bed," answered Mum.
  d "Shall we go out?" suggested Tim.
  e "Good idea!" replied Ella.
  f Jake grumbled, "My head hurts."
  g Lucy asked, "What time is it?"
  h Dad explained, "The toy is broken."
  i Sally demanded, "Why can't I?"
  j Mum replied, "Because it is late."

2. a said
  b asked
  c replied
  d asked
  e answered
  f explained
  g commented
  h argued
  i shouted
  j insisted

Page 12

1. a a
  b an
  c a
  d an
  e a
  f an
  g a
  h a

2. a an
  b a
  c an
  d A
  e an
  f an
  g an

Page 13

1. a quicker
  b longest
  c nicer
  d late
  e hottest
  f fatter
  g angry

2. a funnier
  b closest
  c biggest
  d sunnier
  e happier

Page 14

1. Check your child has placed a mark before Secondly, Finally and As a result.

2. Any sentences which make sense, using the connectives provided.

Page 15

1. Can your child spell the words from memory? Any sentences which contain the words given and make sense.

2. Can your child spell the words from memory? Any sentences which contain the words given and make sense.

Page 16

1. Can your child spell the words from memory?

2. Any sentences which contain the words given, and make sense.

Page 17

1. Can your child spell the words from memory?

2. Any sentences which contain the words given, and make sense.

Page 18

1.
a gladly   f softly
b suddenly   g loudly
c slowly   h sharply
d quickly   i quietly
e beautifully

2.
a thankful   f beautiful
b perfect   g graceful
c slow   h quick
d sudden   i certain
e angry

Page 19

1.
1 Abigail   5 Anthony
2 Aiden   6 Arthur
3 Alice   7 Ashley
4 Amy   8 Attia

2.
a 55   e 29   i 82
b 18   f 12   j 6
c 33   g 50
d 63   h 46

Page 20

1. Can your child spell the words from memory?

2. Any sentences which mean the same as:
a A person who makes a living playing music.
b A person who rewires houses and other electrical installations.
c A person who earns a living putting on magic shows.
d A person who decides how the country, or a local area, is run and organised.
e A person who works out mathematical problems, or teaches others to do so.
f A doctor.
g A person who tests eyes and keeps them healthy.
h A person who carries out technical tasks, such as setting up a lab in a school.

Page 21

1.
a I, my   e We   i his
b you   f my   j their
c I, his   g mine
d them   h I, her

2.
a her   c She   e his
b They   d We   f They

Page 22

1.
a sheep   f puppies
b bees   g lions
c stairs   h geese
d cards   i monkeys
e flowers   j fish

2.
a horses — herd
b birds — flock
c cars — fleet
d books — library
e musicians — group
f dolphins — pod

Page 23

1.
a Joe, my brother, is eight years old.
b For lunch, we had sausages, chips, peas and carrots.
c I'm wearing trousers, a shirt, socks and shoes.
d Actually, it is quite warm today.
e The bag split, so the shopping went everywhere.
f In stories, the knight always kills the dragon.
g You need sugar, flour, eggs and butter to bake a cake.
h Anyway, it was all fine in the end.

2.
a Mrs Smith, my teacher, marked my work.
b My best friends are Chris, Sam and Jo.
c In the end, I chose the blue coat.
d Although it was late, we played one more game.
e Last night, after Dad came home, we watched TV.
f Alex, my best friend, lives next door.
g At the zoo, we saw elephants, lions, camels and giraffes.
h Eventually, I found the missing book.

Page 24

1.
a ~~except~~   e ~~brake~~
b ~~affect~~   f ~~fare~~
c ~~bawl~~   g ~~grate~~
d ~~bury~~

2. Any sentences which contain the words given, and show your child understands the meaning of the word.

Page 25

1.
a 6   c 5   e 1
b 2   d 4   f 3

2.
a Find a small flower pot.
b Fill the pot with soil, leaving a gap at the top.
c Use your finger or a pencil to make a hole about 3 cm deep.
d Drop a sunflower seed into the hole.
e Cover with soil.
f Keep soil just damp until seedling appears.

Page 26

1.
a information   d admiration
b adoration   e condensation
c preparation   f stagnation

2. Any sentences which contain the words given, and show your child understands the meaning of the word.

Page 27

1.
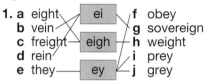
a eight   f obey
b vein   g sovereign
c freight   h weight
d rein   i prey
e they   j grey

2.
a I <u>weighed</u> out a kilogram of apples.
b My dog <u>obeys</u> all my commands.
c I did a <u>survey</u> about which biscuits people like best.
d Father Christmas rides on a <u>sleigh</u>.
e That horse <u>neighed</u> at me!
f My <u>neighbour</u> is called Susan.
g <u>They</u> love swimming in the sea.
h Spiders have <u>eight</u> hairy legs.
i I can see rich <u>veins</u> of chocolate running through this ice cream – delicious!

Page 28

1.
a Understanding something
b Dividing something into smaller pieces
c Something to watch programmes on
d Talking about something
e Finding something difficult to understand
f Entrance fee; admitting something
g A look on someone's face
h Being able to see

2.
a invasion   f expression
b pension   g tension
c mission   h occasion
d session   i passion
e version   j permission
Then any six words chosen, written into sensible sentences.

Page 29

1.
a they run   f we walk
b they swim   g we eat
c we laugh   h they push
d they sleep   i they wish
e they build   j we hope

2.
a They pick the flowers.
b They kick the balls.
c We sharpen the pencils.
d They wash the cars.

ANSWERS

Page 30

1. **a** when **d** but **g** when
   b so **e** because **h** or
   c but **f** while

2. **a** I got a drink, because I was thirsty.
   b Chris wants a skateboard, but Mum said no.
   c Luke was three when I was born.
   d We waited while Dad packed up the car.
   e I could go bowling or I could go swimming.

Page 31

1. First person accounts: b, c, f, h
   Third person accounts: a, d, e, g

2. I live in a small house in Bridge Street. I have a dog and a cat. I play netball and I am learning to play the violin. My best friend is called Leah.

Page 32

The missing prefix is in **bold**.

1. **un**pack
2. **un**well
3. **dis**place
4. **dis**trust
5. **un**fair
6. **un**happy
7. **dis**agree
8. **dis**may
9. **un**load
10. **un**bolt
11. **dis**honest
12. **un**do
13. **dis**arm
14. **dis**charge
15. **dis**please

Page 33

1. disappeared
2. spoke
3. chased
4. brushed
5. painted
6. knocking
7. drinking
8. groaned
9. pushing
10. shining
11. roared
12. crashed
13. flapped
14. hopped
15. came

Page 34

The correct phoneme is in **bold**.

1. m**oo**n
2. tr**ea**t
3. gr**ow**
4. gl**ue**
5. r**oa**d
6. cl**aw**
7. p**ai**nt
8. b**ur**n
9. **ow**l
10. th**ir**sty
11. yesterd**ay**
12. narr**ow**
13. r**ou**nd
14. s**au**cer
15. b**oi**l

Page 35

1. purple
2. a puff of smoke
3. a flame
4. strong and scaly
5. black
6. three green eggs

7. a chirping sound
8. three
9. stroked them with her paws and sang them to sleep
10. happy, pleased

Page 36

1. Where do you come from?
2. What a funny name!
3. The spaceship landed.
4. A door opened slowly.
5. Run for your life!
6. Who is there?
7. What do you want?
8. It's not fair!
9. This is terrible!
10. The sun set in the sky.
11. The bees buzzed near the flowers.
12. How did the car crash?
13. When did the letter come?
14. Stop that at once!
15. We have sausages and chips for tea.

Page 37

1. Little Bo Peep said, "I've lost my sheep."
2. The mouse said, "I ran up the clock."
3. Humpty Dumpty said, "I fell off the wall."
4. Incy Wincy Spider said, "I climbed up the water spout."
5. Little Jack Horner said, "I sat in the corner."
6. "I marched up the hill," said the grand old Duke of York.
7. "I went to London," said Dick Whittington.
8. "I met a wolf," said Little Red Riding Hood.
9. "I climbed a beanstalk," said Jack.
10. "I ran away," said the gingerbread man.
11. Hansel said, "I got lost in a wood."
12. "I went to the ball," Cinderella said.
13. Old King Cole said, "I'm a merry old soul."
14. "I made some tarts," said the Queen of Hearts.
15. "I'm very ugly," the troll said.

Page 38

1. bat cat dog
2. elephant fox goat
3. hen jaguar kangaroo
4. lion monkey ostrich
5. penguin rat seal

6. panda swan zebra
7. beetle donkey hamster mouse
8. donkey giraffe ox worm
9. cat cow crab
10. bear bird bull
11. parrot pelican pike
12. sardine shark snake
13. tiger toad trout turtle
14. gerbil giraffe gnu goat
15. badger bee bird buffalo

Page 39

1. walked
2. hopped
3. carried
4. moved
5. arrived
6. begged
7. copied
8. held
9. brought
10. saw
11. spoke
12. took
13. taught
14. wrote
15. came

Page 40

1. a mother and her child
2. a doctor, astronaut or vet
3. The mother saw that lots of people needed help when she was working as a volunteer at a shelter for homeless people.
4. yes, she loves her job.
5. work hard

Page 41

1. card, tape, paints, glitter glue, elastic
2. draw the design on card
3. cut out eye and mouth holes
4. leave the mask to dry
5. markers and glitter glue

Page 42

1. curious/anxious/surprised, wondering what the noise was
2. scared/frightened/anxious/curious
3. perhaps because she was scared
4. it was protecting the girl
5. probably looking for food

Page 43

1. chairs
2. foxes
3. coaches
4. bushes
5. glasses
6. berries
7. children
8. men
9. bike
10. box
11. bunch
12. dish
13. copy
14. lorry
15. sheep